Problem Solvers

Edited by L. Marder
Senior Lecturer in Mathematics, University of Southam...

No. 10

Laplace Transfo...

Problem Solvers

Laplace Transforms

J. WILLIAMS

Senior Lecturer in Applied Mathematics
University of Exeter

LONDON · GEORGE ALLEN & UNWIN LTD

RUSKIN HOUSE   MUSEUM STREET

First published in 1973

© George Allen & Unwin Ltd, 1973

ISBN 0 04 512020 x *hardback*
      0 04 512021 8 *paper*

To my wife, Anita

Printed in Great Britain
in 10 on 12 pt 'Monophoto' Times Mathematics Series 569
by Page Bros (Norwich) Ltd, Norwich

Contents

Chapter 1

The Laplace Transform

1.1 Definition of Laplace Transform Given a function $F(t)$ defined for all real $t \geqslant 0$, the integral

$$\int_0^\infty e^{-st}F(t)\,dt = \lim_{\varepsilon \to 0+} \lim_{T \to \infty} \int_\varepsilon^T e^{-st}F(t)\,dt \qquad (1.1)$$

if it exists for some values of s, is said to be the *Laplace transform* of $F(t)$. It is written $\mathscr{L}\{F(t)\}$ and determines a function $f(s)$, say, of the parameter s at those values of s for which the integral exists, i.e.

$$\mathscr{L}\{F(t)\} = \int_0^\infty e^{-st}F(t)\,dt = f(s) \qquad (1.2)$$

For the moment we restrict s to real values, in which case it can be shown that if the integral in (1.1) converges for $s = \sigma$ it will converge for all $s \geqslant \sigma$. It is convenient to use a capital letter to denote the *original* function $F(t)$ and the corresponding lower case letter to indicate its Laplace transform $f(s)$.

When $F(t)$ is a *complex* function of the real variable $t \geqslant 0$, we write $F(t) = X(t) + i\,Y(t)$, where $X(t)$ and $Y(t)$ are real functions. Then, provided $x(s)$ and $y(s)$ exist,

$$\mathscr{L}\{F(t)\} = f(s) = \mathscr{L}\{X(t)\} + i\,\mathscr{L}\{Y(t)\} = x(s) + i\,y(s)$$

where $x(s) = \mathscr{L}\{X(t)\}, \quad y(s) = \mathscr{L}\{Y(t)\}$

Problem 1.1 Find $\mathscr{L}\{\cosh pt\}$, $\mathscr{L}\{\sinh pt\}$ where p is a real positive constant.

Solution. Since $\cosh pt = \frac{1}{2}(e^{pt} + e^{-pt})$ we have,

$$\mathscr{L}\{\cosh pt\} = \int_0^\infty e^{-st}\cdot\frac{1}{2}(e^{pt} + e^{-pt})\,dt = \frac{1}{2}\left[-\frac{e^{-(s-p)t}}{s-p} - \frac{e^{-(s+p)t}}{s+p}\right]_0^\infty$$

provided $s \neq p$. When $s > p$ both $e^{-(s-p)t}$ and $e^{-(s+p)t}$ converge to zero as $t \to \infty$. In this case the Laplace transform exists and

$$\mathscr{L}\{\cosh pt\} = \frac{1}{2}\left(\frac{1}{s-p} + \frac{1}{s+p}\right) = \frac{s}{s^2 - p^2}, \qquad s > p$$

When $s < p$, $\lim_{t \to \infty} e^{-(s-p)t}$ does not exist; the integral diverges so that the Laplace transform is *not defined* for $s < p$. Finally when $s = p$, $\mathscr{L}\{\cosh pt\} = \frac{1}{2}\int_0^\infty (1 + e^{-2st})\,dt$ which diverges and so the Laplace transform is again *not defined*. Similarly, since $\sinh pt = \frac{1}{2}(e^{pt} - e^{-pt})$

$$\mathcal{L}\{\sinh pt\} = \frac{1}{2}\int_0^\infty e^{-st}(e^{pt} - e^{-pt})dt = \frac{1}{2}\left(\frac{1}{s-p} - \frac{1}{s+p}\right) = \frac{p}{s^2 - p^2}$$

provided $s > p$; the Laplace transform does not exist for $s \leqslant p$. ☐

Problem 1.2 Find $\mathcal{L}\{\cos qt\}$, $\mathcal{L}\{\sin qt\}$ where q is a real positive constant.

Solution. We have $I = \mathcal{L}\{\cos qt\} = \int_0^\infty e^{-st}\cos qt\, dt$. Integrating by parts, i.e. writing $\int u\, dv = uv - \int v\, du$ with $u = \cos qt$,

$$I = \left[-\frac{e^{-st}}{s}\cos qt\right]_0^\infty - \frac{q}{s}\int_0^\infty e^{-st}\sin qt\, dt = \frac{1}{s} - \frac{q}{s}J \qquad (i)$$

where $J = \mathcal{L}\{\sin qt\}$, provided $s > 0$ so that $\lim_{t \to \infty} e^{-st} = 0$. We again integrate by parts the *same* integral I but this time we use $u = e^{-st}$,

$$I = \left[\frac{e^{-st}}{q}\sin qt\right]_0^\infty + \frac{s}{q}\int_0^\infty e^{-st}\sin qt\, dt = \frac{s}{q}J \qquad (ii)$$

provided $q \neq 0$, $s > 0$. Eliminating J between (i) and (ii)

$$I = \frac{s}{(s^2 + q^2)}, \qquad J = \frac{q}{(s^2 + q^2)}.$$

Alternatively, using Euler's formula for complex numbers, $\cos qt + i\sin qt = e^{iqt}$, we have

$$I + iJ = \int_0^\infty e^{-st}\cos qt\, dt + i\int_0^\infty e^{-st}\sin qt\, dt$$

$$= \int_0^\infty e^{-st}(\cos qt + i\sin qt)\, dt$$

$$= \int_0^\infty e^{-st}e^{iqt}\, dt = \left[\frac{e^{-(s-iq)t}}{(s-iq)}\right]_0^\infty$$

$$= \left[-\frac{e^{-st}(\cos qt + i\sin qt)}{(s-iq)}\right]_0^\infty = 0 + \frac{1}{(s-iq)}$$

when $s > 0$. Therefore,

$$I + iJ = \frac{1}{(s-iq)} = \frac{s + iq}{s^2 + q^2}$$

whence, equating real and imaginary parts, we have

$$I = \mathcal{L}\{\cos qt\} = \frac{s}{s^2 + q^2}, \qquad J = \mathcal{L}\{\sin qt\} = \frac{q}{s^2 + q^2}. \qquad ☐$$

2

1.2 Existence Theorem We need to consider functions $F(t)$ which possess finite discontinuities, because in the applications of Laplace transforms to physical problems these frequently arise. Examples are the unit Heaviside step function and the unit rectangular wave function illustrated in Fig. 1.1. Such functions are said to be *piecewise continuous*.

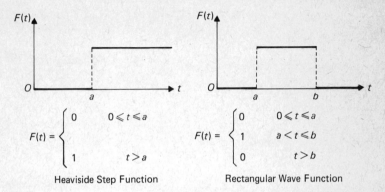

$$F(t) = \begin{cases} 0 & 0 \leqslant t \leqslant a \\ \\ 1 & t > a \end{cases}$$

Heaviside Step Function

$$F(t) = \begin{cases} 0 & 0 \leqslant t \leqslant a \\ 1 & a < t \leqslant b \\ 0 & t > b \end{cases}$$

Rectangular Wave Function

Fig. 1.1

Definition **Piecewise continuity** A function $F(t)$ is *piecewise continuous* in the closed interval $a \leqslant t \leqslant b$ when the interval can be subdivided into a finite number of subintervals, $a \leqslant t \leqslant t_1$, $t_1 \leqslant t \leqslant t_2$, ..., $t_{n-1} \leqslant t \leqslant b$ such that

(i) $F(t)$ is continuous in each open interval

$$t_r < t < t_{r+1}, \qquad r = 0, 1, \ldots, n-1, t_0 \equiv a, t_n \equiv b.$$

(ii) $F(t)$ tends to a *finite* limit as t tends to each end point from within the interval, i.e. for small $\varepsilon > 0$

$$\lim_{\varepsilon \to 0} F(t_r + \varepsilon) = F(t_r+), \lim_{\varepsilon \to 0} F(t_{r+1} - \varepsilon) = F(t_{r+1}-)$$

exist for all $r = 0, 1, \ldots, n-1$.

A function which is piecewise continuous in a finite interval is integrable over that interval.

The next step is to obtain sufficient conditions on $F(t)$ in order that $\mathscr{L}\{F(t)\}$ exists. Since $\int_T^\infty e^{-(s-\sigma)t} \, dt$, $(T \geqslant 0)$ converges for $s > \sigma$, we can use this fact to explore the convergence of the Laplace transform integral $\int_0^\infty e^{-st}F(t) \, dt$ when $\left| e^{-\sigma t}F(t) \right| < M$ for all $t \geqslant T$, T and M being positive constants.

Definition **Exponential Order** A function $F(t)$ is of *exponential order* σ as $t \to \infty$ if constants σ, $M(> 0)$ and $T(> 0)$ can be found such that

3

$$|e^{-\sigma t}F(t)| < M \quad \text{or} \quad |F(t)| < Me^{\sigma t} \qquad \text{for all } t \geqslant T > 0$$

Equivalently, we write

$$F(t) = O(e^{\sigma t}) \qquad \text{as} \quad t \to \infty$$

We now introduce a class of functions which have been called *class $\mathscr{A}$* in the literature, for which the Laplace transform exists.

Definition Functions of class $\mathscr{A}$ A function $F(t)$ is said to belong to class $\mathscr{A}$ when $F(t)$ is of *some* exponential order as $t \to \infty$ and is piecewise continuous over *every* finite interval of $t \geqslant 0$. For such a function we write

$$F(t) \in \text{class } \mathscr{A}$$

Theorem When $F(t) \in$ class $\mathscr{A}$, $\mathscr{L}\{F(t)\}$ exists, provided s is large enough.

To prove the theorem, because $F(t)$ is of exponential order as $t \to \infty$ we can find σ, with positive M and T such that $|F(t)| < Me^{\sigma t}$ for all $t \geqslant T > 0$. Also

$$\mathscr{L}\{F(t)\} = \int_0^\infty e^{-st}F(t) \, dt = \int_0^T e^{-st}F(t) \, dt + \int_T^\infty e^{-st}F(t) \, dt$$

The first integral is integrable, for since $F(t)$ is piecewise continuous, so is $e^{-st}F(t)$. The second integral is absolutely convergent since

$$\left| \int_T^\infty e^{-st}F(t) \, dt \right| < \int_T^\infty \left| e^{-st}F(t) \right| dt < M \int_T^\infty e^{-st}e^{\sigma t} \, dt$$

$$= M \left[-\frac{e^{-(s-\sigma)t}}{(s-\sigma)} \right]_T^\infty = \frac{Me^{-(s-\sigma)T}}{(s-\sigma)}$$

for if $s > \sigma$ then $\lim_{t \to \infty} e^{-(s-\sigma)t} = 0$.

Consequently, $\left| \int_T^\infty e^{-st}F(t) \, dt \right|$ is finite for all $T > 0$ when $s > \sigma$, and so $\mathscr{L}\{F(t)\}$ exists. Thus the condition that $F(t) \in$ class $\mathscr{A}$ is sufficient to ensure the existence of the Laplace transform. *It is not a necessary condition.*

Corollary. Allowing $s \to \infty$ we obtain the result $\lim_{s \to \infty} f(s) = 0$ when $F(t) \in$ class $\mathscr{A}$.

Problem 1.3 For positive integer n, determine which of the following functions belong to class $\mathscr{A}$: (a) t^n, (b) $\cos nt$, (c) $\exp(t^n)$, (d) $t^{-1/n}$

Solution. (a) t^n is continuous in every finite interval in the range $t \geqslant 0$. Again, since $e^t = 1 + t + t^2/2! + \ldots + t^n/n! + \ldots$, it follows that when $t > 0$ each term is positive so that $|t^n| = t^n < n!e^t$ for all $t > 0$, i.e. t^n is of unit exponential order. Consequently, $t^n \in$ class $\mathscr{A}$.

(b) $\cos nt$ is continuous in every finite interval in the range $t \geqslant 0$. Also

4

$|\cos nt| \leqslant 1 = e^0$ for all t so that $\cos nt$ is of zero exponential order for all $t \geqslant 0$, i.e. $\cos nt \in$ class $\mathscr{A}$.

(c) $\exp(t^n)$ is *not* of exponential order. For, with *every* choice of positive constants M, a, we have

$$\left|e^{-at}e^{t^n}\right| = e^{t^n - at} > M,$$

for sufficiently large t.

(d) $t^{-1/n}$ is not a function of class $\mathscr{A}$ because it is not piecewise continuous in *every* finite interval in the range $t \geqslant 0$. This is evident for intervals $0 \leqslant t \leqslant b$ since $t^{-1/n} \to \infty$ as $t \to 0+$. (Nevertheless, it can be shown that the function does possess a Laplace transform.) ☐

Problem 1.4 Show that when n is a positive integer, $\mathscr{L}\{t^n\} = n!/s^{n+1}$ provided $s > 0$.

Solution. By the last problem $t^n \in$ class $\mathscr{A}$ so that the Laplace transform exists. We have

$$\mathscr{L}\{t^n\} = \int_0^\infty e^{-st}t^n \, dt$$

$$= \left[-\frac{1}{s}e^{-st}t^n\right]_0^\infty + \frac{n}{s}\int_0^\infty e^{-st}t^{n-1} \, dt \qquad \text{(by parts)}$$

$$= \frac{n}{s}\int_0^\infty e^{-st}t^{n-1} \, dt \qquad n \geqslant 1, s > 0$$

$$= \frac{n}{s}\mathscr{L}\{t^{n-1}\}$$

We note that this result is true for all $n > 1$ where n is not necessarily an integer. Similarly,

$$\mathscr{L}\{t^{n-1}\} = \frac{(n-1)}{s}\mathscr{L}\{t^{n-2}\}, \qquad n \geqslant 2, s > 0$$

Hence by induction,

$$\mathscr{L}\{t^n\} = \frac{n}{s}\frac{(n-1)}{s}\cdots\frac{1}{s}\mathscr{L}\{t^0\}, \qquad s > 0$$

However

$$\mathscr{L}\{t^0\} = \mathscr{L}\{1\} = \int_0^\infty e^{-st} \, dt = 1/s, \quad s > 0,$$

and so

$$\mathscr{L}\{t^n\} = \frac{n(n-1)\ldots 1}{s\,s\ldots s}\cdot\frac{1}{s} = \frac{n!}{s^{n+1}}, \qquad s > 0 \qquad ☐$$

Problem 1.5 Prove that $\mathcal{L}\{t^{-\frac{1}{2}}\} = (\pi/s)^{\frac{1}{2}}$ and deduce the value of $\mathcal{L}\{t^{\frac{1}{2}k}\}$ where k is a positive odd integer.

Solution. We have $\mathcal{L}\{t^{-\frac{1}{2}}\} = \int_0^\infty e^{-st}t^{-\frac{1}{2}}\,dt$. Putting $st = y^2$, where $s > 0$, we get

$$\mathcal{L}\{t^{-\frac{1}{2}}\} = 2s^{-\frac{1}{2}} \int_0^\infty e^{-y^2}\,dy$$

In books on elementary calculus it is shown that the value of the last integral is $\frac{1}{2}\sqrt{\pi}$. Hence, $\mathcal{L}\{t^{-\frac{1}{2}}\} = (\pi/s)^{\frac{1}{2}}$.

Consider $\mathcal{L}\{t^{\frac{1}{2}k}\}$ where k is a positive odd integer. We write $k = 2m+1$ where m is any positive integer or zero. Using the results of Problem 1.4,

$$\mathcal{L}\{t^{\frac{1}{2}k}\} = \mathcal{L}\{t^{m+\frac{1}{2}}\} = \frac{(m+\frac{1}{2})}{s}\mathcal{L}\{t^{m-\frac{1}{2}}\},$$

$$= \frac{(m+\frac{1}{2})}{s}\frac{(m-\frac{1}{2})}{s}\cdots\frac{(\frac{1}{2})}{s}\mathcal{L}\{t^{-\frac{1}{2}}\}, \qquad \text{by iteration}$$

$$= \frac{(m+\frac{1}{2})(m-\frac{1}{2})\cdots(\frac{1}{2})}{s\quad s\ \cdots\ s}\left(\frac{\pi}{s}\right)^{\frac{1}{2}}$$

$$= \frac{(2m+1)(2m-1)\cdots 3.1}{(2s)^{m+1}}\left(\frac{\pi}{s}\right)^{\frac{1}{2}}$$

$$= \frac{k(k-2)\cdots 3.1}{2^{\frac{1}{2}k+\frac{1}{2}}}\left(\frac{\pi}{s^{k+2}}\right)^{\frac{1}{2}}. \qquad\qquad \square$$

Problem 1.6 Find the Laplace transforms of the following class $\mathcal{A}$ functions:

(i) the Heaviside unit step function $H(t-a)$, $a > 0$ defined by

$$H(t-a) = \begin{cases} 0 & t \leqslant a \\ 1 & t > a \end{cases}$$

(ii) the rectangular wave function $W(t-a, b)$, $0 < a < b$, defined by

$$W(t-a, b) = \begin{cases} 0 & t \leqslant a \\ 1 & a < t \leqslant b \\ 0 & t > b \end{cases}$$

Solution. (i) We have

$$\mathcal{L}\{H(t-a)\} = \int_0^\infty e^{-st}H(t-a)\,dt$$

$$= \int_0^a e^{-st}H(t-a)\,dt + \int_a^\infty e^{-st}H(t-a)\,dt$$

$$= 0 + \int_a^\infty e^{-st}.1\,dt$$

$$= \left[-\frac{1}{s}e^{-st}\right]_a^\infty = \frac{1}{s}e^{-as} \qquad \text{provided } s > 0.$$

It should be noticed that if $a \leqslant 0$, $H(t-a) = 1$ for all $t > 0$, in which case $\mathscr{L}\{H(t-a)\} = \mathscr{L}\{1\} = 1/s$, $s > 0$ when $a \leqslant 0$.

(ii) For the rectangular wave function where $b > a > 0$,

$$\mathscr{L}\{W(t-a, b)\} = \left(\int_0^a + \int_a^b + \int_b^\infty\right) e^{-st} W(t-a, b) \, dt$$

where the range of integration has been split into the three ranges of t over which W is separately defined. In the first and last of these W is zero, whereas $W = 1$ in the middle range, so that

$$\mathscr{L}\{W(t-a, b)\} = \int_a^b e^{-st} \, dt = \left[-\frac{1}{s} e^{-st}\right]_a^b = \frac{1}{s}(e^{-as} - e^{-bs}), \quad s > 0.$$

This result is obvious when it is realized that an alternative representation of W is simply

$$W(t-a, b) = H(t-a) - H(t-b) \qquad \square$$

Problem 1.7   Find the Laplace transform of the Dirac delta function $\delta(t)$, where $\delta(t) = 0$ $(t \neq 0)$, $\int_0^\infty \delta(t) \, dt = 1$.

Solution. Consider the function $W(t, \varepsilon)/\varepsilon$, $\varepsilon > 0$ where W is the rectangular wave function defined in the previous problem. We have

$$\frac{1}{\varepsilon} W(t, \varepsilon) = \begin{cases} 1/\varepsilon, 0 < t \leqslant \varepsilon, \varepsilon > 0 \\ 0, t > \varepsilon \end{cases}$$

from which it follows that $\int_0^\infty (W(t, \varepsilon)/\varepsilon) \, dt = 1$ independently of ε. The Dirac delta function $\delta(t)$ is defined by

$$\delta(t) = \lim_{\varepsilon \to 0} W(t, \varepsilon)/\varepsilon$$

so that $\delta(t) \to \infty$ as $t \to 0$ whereas $\int_0^\infty \delta(t) \, dt = 1$. Using the result from the last problem, we have

$$\mathscr{L}\left\{\frac{1}{\varepsilon} W(t, \varepsilon)\right\} = \frac{1}{\varepsilon s}(1 - e^{-s\varepsilon})$$

Assuming that taking limits under the Laplace transform is justified, we have

$$\mathscr{L}\{\delta(t)\} = \lim_{\varepsilon \to 0} \frac{1}{\varepsilon s}(1 - e^{-s\varepsilon})$$

$$= \lim_{\varepsilon \to 0} \frac{1}{\varepsilon s}(s\varepsilon - \tfrac{1}{2}s^2\varepsilon^2 + \ldots) = 1$$

i.e. The delta function has Laplace transform *unity*. $\qquad \square$

1.3 Operational Rules of Laplace Transforms   We now consider a

7

number of linear operations, listed herein as *rules*, which can be applied to Laplace transforms. In this way new transforms may be generated. The first is concerned with addition, the second with magnification, the third with translation of the function $F(t)$ and the fourth with translation of $f(s)$. Further rules involve multiplication, differentiation and integration. After description the rules are referred to by number and for easy reference are tabulated towards the end of the book on pages 85–87.

Rule 1   Rule of Addition   Let $F_r(t)$, $r = 1, \ldots, n$ be n functions such that $\mathscr{L}\{F_r(t)\} = f_r(s)$ when $s > \sigma_r$. Given any n constants a_r we have

$$\mathscr{L}\{a_1 F_1(t) + a_2 F_2(t) + \ldots + a_n F_n(t)\} = a_1 f_1(s) + a_2 f_2(s) + \ldots + a_n f_n(s)$$

for $s > \max(\sigma_1, \sigma_2, \ldots, \sigma_n)$.

Problem 1.8   Find the Laplace transforms of (i) $\sin^2 pt$, (ii) $\sin^3 pt$, (iii) $\sin at \cos bt$.

Solution. (i) We write $\sin^2 pt = \frac{1}{2}(1 - \cos 2pt)$ and use the above rule of addition to obtain

$$\mathscr{L}\{\sin^2 pt\} = \mathscr{L}\{\tfrac{1}{2}(1 - \cos 2pt)\} = \tfrac{1}{2}\mathscr{L}\{1\} - \tfrac{1}{2}\mathscr{L}\{\cos 2pt\}$$

$$= \frac{1}{2}\left(\frac{1}{s}\right) - \frac{1}{2}\left(\frac{s}{s^2 + 4p^2}\right) = \frac{2p^2}{s(s^2 + 4p^2)}, \qquad s > 0.$$

(ii) Using the result of Problem 1.2, and $4\sin^3 pt = 3\sin pt - \sin 3pt$, consequently

$$\mathscr{L}\{\sin^3 pt\} = \tfrac{3}{4}\mathscr{L}\{\sin pt\} - \tfrac{1}{4}\mathscr{L}\{\sin 3pt\}$$

$$= \frac{3}{4}\left(\frac{p}{s^2 + p^2}\right) - \frac{1}{4}\left(\frac{3p}{s^2 + 9p^2}\right) = \frac{6p^3}{(s^2 + p^2)(s^2 + 9p^2)}, \qquad s > 0.$$

(iii) $\sin at \cos bt = \frac{1}{2}\{\sin(a+b)t + \sin(a-b)t\}$ so that

$$\mathscr{L}\{\sin at \cos bt\} = \tfrac{1}{2}\mathscr{L}\{\sin(a+b)t\} + \tfrac{1}{2}\mathscr{L}\{\sin(a-b)t\}$$

$$= \frac{1}{2}\left(\frac{a+b}{s^2 + (a+b)^2} + \frac{a-b}{s^2 + (a-b)^2}\right)$$

$$= \frac{a(s^2 + a^2 - b^2)}{(s^2 + (a+b)^2)(s^2 + (a-b)^2)} \qquad \square$$

Problem 1.9   Find $\mathscr{L}\{t^{-\frac{1}{2}}\cos at^{\frac{1}{2}}\}$.

Solution.

$$t^{-\frac{1}{2}}\cos at^{\frac{1}{2}} = t^{-\frac{1}{2}}\left(1 - \frac{a^2 t}{2!} + \frac{a^4 t^2}{4!} - \ldots + (-1)^n \frac{a^{2n} t^n}{(2n)!} + \ldots\right)$$

8

Consider $\mathscr{L}\{(-1)^n a^{2n} t^{n-\frac{1}{2}}/(2n)!\}$. Using the result of Problem 1.5,

$$\mathscr{L}\{t^{n-\frac{1}{2}}\} = \frac{(2n-1)(2n-3)\ldots 3.1}{(2s)^n}\left(\frac{\pi}{s}\right)^{\frac{1}{2}}$$

$$= \frac{(2n)!}{(2n)(2n-2)\ldots 2(2s)^n}\left(\frac{\pi}{s}\right)^{\frac{1}{2}} = \frac{(2n)!}{n!(4s)^n}\left(\frac{\pi}{s}\right)^{\frac{1}{2}}$$

so that

$$\mathscr{L}\left\{(-1)^n\frac{a^{2n}t^{n-\frac{1}{2}}}{(2n)!}\right\} = \frac{(-1)^n}{n!}\left(\frac{a^2}{4s}\right)^n\left(\frac{\pi}{s}\right)^{\frac{1}{2}}$$

Hence

$$\mathscr{L}\{t^{-\frac{1}{2}}\cos at^{\frac{1}{2}}\} = \left(\frac{\pi}{s}\right)^{\frac{1}{2}}\left(1-\frac{a^2}{4s}+\frac{1}{2!}\left(\frac{a^2}{4s}\right)^2 - \ldots + \frac{(-1)^n}{n!}\left(\frac{a^2}{4s}\right)^n + \ldots\right)$$

$$= \left(\frac{\pi}{s}\right)^{\frac{1}{2}}e^{-a^2/4s}.$$

The series is convergent for all $s > 0$ and so the operation of term by term summation is valid. $\square$

Rule 2   Rule of Scale   Given $a > 0$ with $\mathscr{L}\{F(t)\} = f(s)$ for $s > \sigma$, the substitution $t = aT$ leads to

$$\mathscr{L}\{F(at)\} = a^{-1}f(s/a) \text{ when } s > a\sigma.$$

Problem 1.10   For the Bessel function of the first kind and zero order defined by $J_0(t) = (1/\pi)\int_0^\pi \cos(t \sin \theta)\, d\theta$ determine $\mathscr{L}\{J_0(at)\}$, $a > 0$.

Solution. We first determine $\mathscr{L}\{J_0(t)\}$ and use the Rule of Scale to write down $\mathscr{L}\{J_0(at)\}$. Now,

$$\mathscr{L}\{J_0(t)\} = \frac{1}{\pi}\int_0^\infty e^{-st}\,dt\int_0^\pi \cos(t \sin \theta)\, d\theta$$

Inverting the order of integration (which is permissible because the integral is absolutely convergent when $s > 0$),

$$\mathscr{L}\{J_0(t)\} = \frac{1}{\pi}\int_0^\pi d\theta\int_0^\infty e^{-st}\cos(t \sin \theta)\, d\theta = \frac{1}{\pi}\int_0^\pi \frac{s}{s^2+\sin^2 \theta}\, d\theta$$

$$= \frac{2s}{\pi}\int_0^{\frac{1}{2}\pi} \frac{\sec^2 \theta}{s^2+(s^2+1)\tan^2 \theta}\, d\theta$$

$$= \frac{2}{\pi\sqrt{(s^2+1)}}\left[\tan^{-1}\left(\frac{\sqrt{(s^2+1)}}{s}\tan \theta\right)\right]_0^{\frac{1}{2}\pi} = \frac{1}{\sqrt{(s^2+1)}}$$

Thus

$$\mathcal{L}\{J_0(at)\} = \frac{1}{a\sqrt{[(s/a)^2+1]}} = \frac{1}{\sqrt{(s^2+a^2)}}, \qquad a > 0 \qquad \square$$

Rule 3 Rule of Shift in the Transform Function Given $f(s) = \int_0^\infty e^{-st}F(t)\,dt$ for $s > \sigma$, then $f(s+\omega) = \int_0^\infty e^{-(s+\omega)t}F(t)\,dt = \mathcal{L}\{e^{-\omega t}F(t)\}$ for $s > \sigma - \omega$ when ω is a real constant. The *transform* function $f(s)$ has been *translated* or *shifted* to a new origin at $s = -\omega$ where ω is here considered real.

If ω is complex we write $\omega = \alpha - i\beta$ where α and β are real. Assuming $F(t)$ is a real function of the real variable t,

$$f(s+\alpha-i\beta) = \mathcal{L}\{e^{-(\alpha-i\beta)t}F(t)\}$$
$$= \mathcal{L}\{e^{-\alpha t}\cos\beta t\,F(t)\}+i\,\mathcal{L}\{e^{-\alpha t}\sin\beta t\,F(t)\}$$

Separating real and imaginary parts, we have

$$\mathcal{L}\{e^{-\alpha t}\cos\beta t\,F(t)\} = \mathrm{Re}\,f(s+\alpha-i\beta),$$
$$\mathcal{L}\{e^{-\alpha t}\sin\beta t\,F(t)\} = \mathrm{Im}\,f(s+\alpha-i\beta).$$

Problem 1.11 Evaluate (i) $\mathcal{L}\{e^{at}+2e^{-\frac{1}{2}at}\cos\frac{1}{2}\sqrt{3}at\}$, (ii) $\mathcal{L}\{\cos bt\cosh at - \sin bt\sinh at\}$.

Solution. (i) If $f(s) = \mathcal{L}\{1\} = 1/s, s > 0$, then

$$\mathcal{L}\{e^{at}\} = f(s-a) = 1/(s-a), \qquad s > a$$
$$\mathcal{L}\{e^{-\frac{1}{2}at}\cos\frac{1}{2}\sqrt{3}at\} = g(s+\tfrac{1}{2}a)$$

where $\quad g(s) = \mathcal{L}\{\cos\frac{1}{2}\sqrt{3}at\} = s/(s^2+\tfrac{3}{4}a^2), \qquad s > 0$

$$= \frac{s+\frac{1}{2}a}{(s+\frac{1}{2}a)^2+\frac{3}{4}a^2} = \frac{s+\frac{1}{2}a}{s^2+as+a^2}, \qquad s > \tfrac{1}{2}a$$

$$\mathcal{L}\{e^{at}+2e^{-\frac{1}{2}at}\cos\tfrac{1}{2}\sqrt{3}at\} = \frac{1}{s-a}+\frac{2s+a}{s^2+as+a^2}, \qquad s > a$$

$$= \frac{3s^2}{(s^3-a^3)}$$

Alternatively, we could have used the extension to Rule 3 to write

$$\mathcal{L}\{e^{-\frac{1}{2}at}\cos\tfrac{1}{2}\sqrt{3}at\} = \mathrm{Re}[1/(s+\tfrac{1}{2}a+\tfrac{1}{2}ia\sqrt{3})] = (s+\tfrac{1}{2}a)/(s^2+as+a^2)$$

(ii) Using $\mathcal{L}\{\cos bt\} = s/(s^2+b^2), \qquad s > 0,$

$$\mathcal{L}\{\cosh at\cos bt\} = \mathcal{L}\{\tfrac{1}{2}(e^{at}+e^{-at})\cos bt\}$$

$$= \frac{1}{2}\left(\frac{s-a}{(s-a)^2+b^2}+\frac{s+a}{(s+a)^2+b^2}\right), \qquad s > a > 0$$

by Rule 3. Again, since $\mathcal{L}\{\sin bt\} = b/(s^2+b^2)$, $s > 0$,

$$\mathcal{L}\{\sinh at \sin bt\} = \mathcal{L}\{\tfrac{1}{2}(e^{at}-e^{-at})\sin bt\}$$

$$= \tfrac{1}{2}\left(\frac{b}{(s-a)^2+b^2} - \frac{b}{(s+a)^2+b^2}\right), \qquad s > a,$$

Hence,

$$\mathcal{L}\{\cos bt \cosh at - \sin bt \sinh at\} = \tfrac{1}{2}\left(\frac{s-a-b}{(s-a)^2+b^2} + \frac{s+a+b}{(s+a)^2+b^2}\right). \qquad \square$$

Problem 1.12 Evaluate $\mathcal{L}\{e^{at}t^n\}$ where n is a positive integer. Deduce expressions for $\mathcal{L}\{t^n\cos \alpha t\}$ and $\mathcal{L}\{t^n\sin \alpha t\}$, $\alpha > 0$.

Solution. In Problem 1.4 we showed that $\mathcal{L}\{t^n\} = n!/s^{n+1}$, $s > 0$. Hence, using Rule 3,

$$\mathcal{L}\{e^{at}t^n\} = n!/(s-a)^{n+1}, \qquad s > a$$

Now write $a = i\alpha$ where α is real and positive and a is purely imaginary. Since $e^{i\alpha t} = \cos \alpha t + i \sin \alpha t$,

$$\mathcal{L}\{(\cos \alpha t + i \sin \alpha t)t^n\} = n!/(s-i\alpha)^{n+1}, \qquad s > 0$$

Therefore, to deduce the required results we evaluate the real and imaginary parts of $(s-i\alpha)^{-n-1}$. To do this we find the positive values for r and θ satisfying $s = r\cos\theta$, $\alpha = r\sin\theta$, i.e. $r = \sqrt{(s^2+\alpha^2)}$, $\tan\theta = \alpha/s$, where $0 < \theta < \tfrac{1}{2}\pi$, since α and s are both positive. Using Demoivre's theorem,

$$1/(s-i\alpha) = (\cos\theta + i\sin\theta)/r$$

$$\mathcal{L}\{(\cos \alpha t + i \sin \alpha t)t^n\} = n![\cos(n+1)\theta + i\sin(n+1)\theta]r^{-n-1}$$

Separating real and imaginary parts we have

$$\mathcal{L}\{t^n\cos \alpha t\} = \frac{n!\cos(n+1)\theta}{(s^2+\alpha^2)^{\frac{1}{2}(n+1)}} \qquad \mathcal{L}\{t^n\sin \alpha t\} = \frac{n!\sin(n+1)\theta}{(s^2+\alpha^2)^{\frac{1}{2}(n+1)}}$$

where $\theta = \tan^{-1}(\alpha/s)$.

Rule 4   Rule of Shift in the Original Function   Given a function $G(t)$ where $\mathcal{L}\{G(t)\} = g(s)$ when $s > \sigma$ we have for a constant $T > 0$,

$$\mathcal{L}\{G(t+T)\} = \int_0^\infty e^{-st}G(t+T)\,dt = e^{sT}\int_T^\infty e^{-st}G(t)\,dt$$

$$= e^{sT}\left(g(s) - \int_0^T e^{-st}G(t)\,dt\right), \qquad s > \sigma, \qquad T > 0$$
$$\text{(i)}$$

which is the Laplace transform of the function $G(t)$ translated a distance $-T$ relative to $t = 0$; a finite Laplace integral is thereby introduced. For translation to the right of the origin put $-T = \tau > 0$ so that

11

$$\mathscr{L}\{G(t-\tau)\} = e^{-s\tau}\left(g(s)+\int_0^\tau e^{st}G(-t)\,dt\right), \qquad s > \sigma, \qquad \tau > 0 \qquad \text{(ii)}$$

Using the Heaviside step function defined in Problem 1.6 we can construct functions which vanish for all $t < 0$ in which case the finite integral in (ii) is eliminated. Consider $G(t) = H(t)F(t)$, we have $G(t) \equiv F(t)$ for all $t > 0$, $G(t) = 0$ for all $t \leq 0$. Moreover,

$$g(s) = \mathscr{L}\{G(t)\} = \mathscr{L}\{H(t)F(t)\} = \mathscr{L}\{F(t) = f(s)$$

so that (ii) becomes

$$\mathscr{L}\{H(t-\tau)F(t-\tau)\} = e^{-st}f(s) \qquad \text{(iii)}$$

Whereas Rule 3 is used to evaluate certain types of transforms, Rule 4 is usually employed to find the *original* function given its transform. This will be explored in Chapter 2.

Problem 1.13 Evaluate $\mathscr{L}\{F(t)\}$ where

$$F(t) = \begin{cases} 0 & 0 \leq t \leq a \\ t^n & t > a \end{cases}$$

Solution. We can write $F(t) = H(t-a)t^n$. Also using the binomial theorem

$$t^n = (t-a+a)^n = (t-a)^n + na(t-a)^{n-1} + \ldots$$
$$+ \frac{n!}{m!(n-m)!}a^{n-m}(t-a)^m + \ldots + a^n$$

$$\mathscr{L}\{F(t)\} = \mathscr{L}\{H(t-a)(t-a)^n\} + na\mathscr{L}\{H(t-a)(t-a)^{n-1}\} + \ldots$$
$$+ \frac{n!a^{n-m}}{m!(n-m)!}\mathscr{L}\{H(t-a)(t-a)^m\} + \ldots + a^n\mathscr{L}\{H(t-a)\}$$

Applying Rule 4 to a general term of this series,

$$\mathscr{L}\{H(t-a)(t-a)^m\} = e^{-sa}\mathscr{L}\{t^m\}, \qquad a > 0, \ s > 0$$
$$= e^{-sa}m!/s^{m+1}$$

i.e.
$$\mathscr{L}\{F(t)\} = e^{-sa}n!s^{-(n+1)}\left(1+as+\frac{a^2s^2}{2!}+\ldots+\frac{a^ns^n}{n!}\right).$$

□

Problem 1.14 Find the Laplace transform of $J(t)$ which is represented in Fig. 1.2 by $APQ'P'Q''P''Q'''$ taken along the sides of three equilateral triangles each of side $2a$ and based on Ot where $OQ = b < a$.

Solution. Using Rule 4 we need only evaluate the Laplace transform of the function corresponding to the first truncated triangle APQ'. First, for the element AP, we define

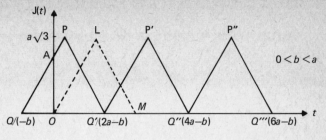

Fig. 1.2

$$F(t) = F_1(t) = \begin{cases} = \sqrt{3}(t+b), & 0 \leqslant t \leqslant a-b \\ = 0 & t > a-b \end{cases}$$

so that

$$\mathscr{L}\{AP\} \equiv \mathscr{L}\{F_1(t)\} = \sqrt{3}\int_0^{a-b}(t+b)e^{-st}\,dt$$

$$= \sqrt{3}\left[-\frac{(t+b)}{s}e^{-st}\right]_0^{a-b} + \frac{\sqrt{3}}{s}\int_0^{a-b}e^{-st}\,dt$$

$$= \frac{\sqrt{3}}{s}(b-ae^{-(a-b)s}) + \frac{\sqrt{3}}{s^2}[e^{-st}]_0^{a-b}$$

$$= \sqrt{3}(b-ae^{-(a-b)s})s^{-1} + \sqrt{3}(1-e^{-(a-b)s})s^{-2} \qquad \text{(i)}$$

Similarly, for the segment PQ' we define

$$F(t) = F_2(t) = \begin{cases} \sqrt{3}(2a-b-t) & a-b \leqslant t \leqslant 2a-b \\ 0 & 0 < t < a-b \text{ or } t > 2a-b \end{cases}$$

Consequently,

$$\mathscr{L}\{PQ'\} \equiv \mathscr{L}\{F_2(t)\} = \sqrt{3}\int_{a-b}^{2a+b}(2a-b-t)e^{-st}\,dt$$

$$= \sqrt{3}\left[-\frac{(2a-b-t)}{s}e^{-st}\right]_{a-b}^{2a-b} - \frac{\sqrt{3}}{s}\int_{a-b}^{2a-b}e^{-st}\,dt$$

$$= \sqrt{3}as^{-1}e^{-(a-b)s} + \sqrt{3}(e^{-(2a-b)s} - e^{-(a-b)s})s^{-2} \qquad \text{(ii)}$$

The Laplace transform of the function represented by APQ' is obviously the sum of (i) and (ii), i.e.

$$\mathscr{L}\{APQ'\} = \sqrt{3}bs^{-1} + \sqrt{3}(1 - 2e^{-(a-b)s} + e^{-(2a-b)s})s^{-2} \qquad \text{(iii)}$$

Moreover, if we put $b = 0$ we obtain the Laplace transform of the function represented by the triangle OLM (Indicated in Fig. 1.2 by a dotted line), i.e.

13

$$\mathcal{L}\{OLM\} = \sqrt{3}(1-2e^{-as}+e^{-2as})/s^2 = \sqrt{3}(1-e^{-as})^2/s^2$$

The triangles $Q'P'Q''$ and $Q''P''Q'''$ can be obtained by sliding OLM along Ot through distances $2a-b$ and $4a-b$ respectively. Therefore, using Rule 4, we have

$$\mathcal{L}\{Q'P'Q''\} = e^{-(2a-b)s}\mathcal{L}\{OLM\} = \sqrt{3}e^{-(2a-b)s}(1-e^{-as})^2/s^2 \quad \text{(iv)}$$

$$\mathcal{L}\{Q''P''Q'''\} = e^{-(4a-b)s}\mathcal{L}\{OLM\} = \sqrt{3}e^{-(4a-b)s}(1-e^{-as})^2/s^2 \quad \text{(v)}$$

Finally, $\mathcal{L}\{J(t)\} = \mathcal{L}\{APQ'+Q'P'Q''+Q''P''Q'''\}$ is the sum of (iii), (iv), and (v) so that

$$\mathcal{L}\{J(t)\} = \sqrt{3}bs^{-1}+\sqrt{3}s^{-2}[1-2e^{-(a-b)s}+e^{-(2a-b)s}+(e^{-(2a-b)s}$$
$$+e^{-(4a-b)s})(1-e^{-as})^2] \qquad \square$$

1.4 Laplace Transform of $M(t)F(t)$ where $M(t)$ is a polynomial.

Rule 5 Given a polynomial function $M(t)$ with $\mathcal{L}\{F(t)\} = f(s)$ for $s > \sigma$ we have

$$\mathcal{L}\{M(t)F(t)\} = M(-\mathcal{D})f(s) \text{ where } \mathcal{D} \equiv d/ds$$

For when $M(t)$ is of the form $\sum\limits_{r=0}^{n} a_r t^r$ where a_r is a constant for each r and $\mathcal{D}^r f(s) = \int_0^\infty (-t)^r e^{-st}F(t)\,dt, s > \sigma$ it follows that

$$M(-\mathcal{D})f(s) = \sum_{r=0}^{n} a_r(-\mathcal{D})^r f(s) = \int_0^\infty e^{-st}M(t)F(t)\,dt$$

In particular,

$$\mathcal{L}\{(a-t)F(t)\} = (a+\mathcal{D})f(s) = e^{-as}\mathcal{D}(e^{as}f(s))$$

and by induction $\mathcal{L}\{(a-t)^n F(t)\} = e^{-as}\mathcal{D}^n(e^{as}f(s))$ which when $a = 0$ reduces to $\mathcal{L}\{t^n F(t)\} = (-\mathcal{D})^n f(s)$.

Problem 1.15 Evaluate $\mathcal{L}\{t^n e^{at}\}$

Solution. Since $\mathcal{L}\{e^{at}\} = 1/(s-a)$ for $s > a$, using Rule 5,

$$\mathcal{L}\{t^n e^{at}\} = (-1)^n \mathcal{D}^n(s-a)^{-1} = n!(s-a)^{-n-1}, s > a. \qquad \square$$

(Another solution was given in Problem 1.12.)

Problem 1.16 Given that the Laplace transform of the Bessel function $J_0(t)$ is $(s^2+1)^{-\frac{1}{2}}$, (see Problem 1.10), determine $\mathcal{L}\{t^2 J_0(t)\}$.

Solution. Using Rule 5,

$$\mathcal{L}\{t^2 J_0(t)\} = \mathcal{D}^2 \mathcal{L}\{J_0(t)\}$$
$$= \mathcal{D}^2(s^2+1)^{-\frac{1}{2}} = \mathcal{D}(-s(s^2+1)^{-\frac{3}{2}})$$
$$= (2s^2-1)(s^2+1)^{-\frac{5}{2}} \qquad \square$$

14

Problem 1.17 Given $a > 0$, evaluate $\mathscr{L}\{t^n\cos at\}$ and $\mathscr{L}\{t^n\sin at\}$ when $n = 1, 2$ and 3. Hence find $F(t)$ for which $\mathscr{L}\{F(t)\}$ has the value (i) $8a^5/(s^2+a^2)^3$, (ii) $48a^7/(s^2+a^2)^4$.

Solution. Starting from the fundamental results

$$\mathscr{L}\{\cos at\} = \frac{s}{(s^2+a^2)}, \qquad \mathscr{L}\{\sin at\} = \frac{a}{(s^2+a^2)}$$

and making continued application of Rule 5 with $\mathscr{D} \equiv d/ds$,

$$\mathscr{L}\{t\cos at\} = -\mathscr{D}\mathscr{L}\{\cos at\} = 2s^2(s^2+a^2)^{-2} - (s^2+a^2)^{-1}$$
$$= (s^2+a^2)^{-1} - 2a^2(s^2+a^2)^{-2} \tag{i}$$
$$\mathscr{L}\{t^2\cos at\} = -\mathscr{D}\mathscr{L}\{t\cos at\} = 2s(s^2+a^2)^{-2} - 8a^2s(s^2+a^2)^{-3} \tag{ii}$$
$$\mathscr{L}\{t^3\cos at\} = -\mathscr{D}\mathscr{L}\{t^2\cos at\} = 6(s^2+a^2)^{-2} - 48a^2(s^2+a^2)^{-3}$$
$$+ 48a^4(s^2+a^2)^{-4} \tag{iii}$$
$$\mathscr{L}\{t\sin at\} = -\mathscr{D}\mathscr{L}\{\sin at\} = 2as(s^2+a^2)^{-2} \tag{iv}$$
$$\mathscr{L}\{t^2\sin at\} = 6a(s^2+a^2)^{-2} - 8a^3(s^2+a^2)^{-3} \tag{v}$$
$$\mathscr{L}\{t^3\sin at\} = 24as(s^2+a^2)^{-3} - 48a^3s(s^2+a^2)^{-4} \tag{vi}$$

From (i),

$$2a^3(s^2+a^2)^{-2} = a(s^2+a^2)^{-1} - \mathscr{L}\{at\cos at\} = \mathscr{L}\{\sin at - at\cos at\} \tag{vii}$$

Using (v), and eliminating $6a^3(s^2+a^2)^{-2}$ by (vii), we find

$$8a^5(s^2+a^2)^{-3} = 6a^3(s^2+a^2)^{-2} - \mathscr{L}\{a^2t^2\sin at\}$$
$$= 3\mathscr{L}\{\sin at - at\cos at\} - \mathscr{L}\{a^2t^2\sin at\}$$
$$= \mathscr{L}\{3\sin at - 3at\cos at - a^2t^2\sin at\} \tag{viii}$$

Similarly from (iii), (viii) and (vii)

$$48a^7(s^2+a^2)^{-4} = \mathscr{L}\{a^3t^3\cos at\} + 48a^5(s^2+a^2)^{-3} - 6a^3(s^2+a^2)^{-2}$$
$$= \mathscr{L}\{a^3t^3\cos at\} + 6\mathscr{L}\{3\sin at - 3at\cos at - a^2t^2\sin at\}$$
$$- 3\mathscr{L}\{\sin at - at\cos at\}$$
$$= \mathscr{L}\{a^3t^3\cos at - 6a^2t^2\sin at - 15at\cos at + 15\sin at\} \qquad \square$$

1.5 Laplace Transform of $F(t)/(t+a)$, $a \geqslant 0$.

Rule 6 Given $\mathscr{L}\{F(t)\} = f(s)$ for $s > \sigma$, $a \geqslant 0$,

$$\mathscr{L}\{F(t)/(t+a)\} = I = e^{sa}\int_s^\infty e^{-xa} f(x)\, dx$$

To prove this result, we have with $\mathscr{D} \equiv d/ds$,

$$(\mathscr{D}-a)\int_0^\infty e^{-st}[F(t)/(t+a)]\, dt = -\int_0^\infty e^{-st}F(t)\, dt = -f(s)$$

15

i.e.

$$(\mathscr{D} - a)I = e^{sa}\mathscr{D}(e^{-as}I) = -f(s)$$

Integrating, $e^{-as}I = -\int^s e^{-xa} f(x)\, dx +$ constant. Invoking the corollary on page 4, $I \to 0$ as $s \to \infty$ i.e.

$$I = e^{as}\int_s^\infty e^{-xa} f(x)\, dx.$$

If $a = 0$ the corresponding result is

$$\mathscr{L}\{t^{-1}F(t)\} = \int_s^\infty f(x)\, dx$$

provided $\lim\limits_{t \to 0+} F(t)/t$, exists.

Problem 1.18 Evaluate $\sin \lambda t/(t+a)$, $a \geqslant 0$.

Solution. We have $\mathscr{L}\{\sin \lambda t\} = \lambda/(s^2 + \lambda^2)$, $s > 0$. Therefore, by Rule 6

$$\mathscr{L}\left\{\frac{\sin \lambda t}{t+a}\right\} = e^{sa}\int_s^\infty \frac{e^{-ax}\lambda\, dx}{x^2 + \lambda^2}$$

In the case when $a = 0$, since $\lim\limits_{t \to 0+} \sin \lambda t/t = \lambda < \infty$,

$$\mathscr{L}\left\{\frac{\sin \lambda t}{t}\right\} = \int_s^\infty \frac{\lambda dx}{x^2 + \lambda^2} = \left[\tan^{-1}\frac{x}{\lambda}\right]_s^\infty$$

$$= \tfrac{1}{2}\pi - \tan^{-1}\frac{s}{\lambda} = \tan^{-1}\frac{\lambda}{s} \quad s > 0$$

When $a > 0$ we write $\int_s^\infty [e^{-ax}/(x^2 + \lambda^2)]dx = J$. Hence,

$$\frac{d^2 J}{da^2} + \lambda^2 J = \int_s^\infty e^{-ax} dx = \frac{e^{-as}}{a}$$

Using the method of variation of parameters we seek a solution for J in the form $J = A(a)\cos \lambda a + B(a)\sin \lambda a$. Assuming $(dA/da)\cos \lambda a + (dB/da)\sin \lambda a = 0$, we find on substitution that $\lambda(dB/da)\cos \lambda a - \lambda(dA/da)\sin \lambda a = e^{-as}/a$. Solving for the derivatives of A and B and integrating we have

$$J = \sin \lambda a\left(B_0 + \int_0^a \frac{e^{-us}}{\lambda u}\cos \lambda u\, du\right) + \cos \lambda a\left(A_0 - \int_0^a \frac{e^{-us}}{\lambda u}\sin \lambda u\, du\right)$$

$$= B_0 \sin \lambda a + A_0 \cos \lambda a + \int_0^a \frac{e^{-us}}{\lambda u}\sin \lambda(a-u)\, du$$

where $A_0 \equiv A(0)$, $B_0 \equiv B(0)$ are constants. Putting $a = 0$, $J = \lambda^{-1}\tan^{-1}(\lambda/s) = A_0$. Also since J is an *even* function of λ we must have $B_0 = $ so that

16

$$\mathscr{L}\left\{\frac{\sin \lambda t}{t+a}\right\} = \lambda e^{sa} J = s^{sa}\tan^{-1}(\lambda/s)\cos \lambda a + \int_0^a e^{-(u-s)a}\sin \lambda(a-u)\,du/u. \quad \square$$

1.6 Laplace Transforms of Derivatives   Assuming that $\mathscr{L}\{F(t)\} = f(s)$ for $s > \sigma$ we have:

Rule 7   Given that
    (i) $F(t)$ is continuous for all $t > 0$
    (ii) $F(t) = O(e^{\sigma t})$ as $t \to \infty$
    (iii) $F'(t) \in$ class $\mathscr{A}$, then

$$\mathscr{L}\{F'(t)\} = sf(s) - F(0+) \qquad \text{for } s > \sigma$$

To prove this result we have, integrating by parts (valid because $F(t)$ is continuous) within the limit operations

$$\mathscr{L}\{F'(t)\} = \lim_{T \to \infty} \lim_{\varepsilon \to 0+} \int_\varepsilon^T e^{-st}F'(t)\,dt$$

$$= \lim_{T \to \infty} \lim_{\varepsilon \to 0+} \left\{ \left[e^{-st}F(t)\right]_\varepsilon^T + s\int_\varepsilon^T e^{-st}F(t)\,dt \right\}$$

$$= -F(0+) + sf(s)$$

since $\lim_{t = T \to \infty} e^{-st}F(t) = 0$ when $s > \sigma$, $\lim_{t = \varepsilon \to 0+} e^{-st}F(t) = F(0+)$ and $\lim_{T \to \infty} \lim_{\varepsilon \to 0+} \int_\varepsilon^T e^{-st}F(t)\,dt = \mathscr{L}\{F(t)\} = f(s)$.

If $F(t)$ is also continuous at $t = 0$, then $F(0+) = F(0)$ in which case,

$$\mathscr{L}\{F'(t)\} = sf(s) - F(0)$$

Rule 8   Given that $F(t), F'(t), \ldots, F^{(n-1)}(t)$ are each continuous for all $t > 0$ and of exponential order while $F^{(n)}(t) \in$ class $\mathscr{A}$, we have, by repeated application of Rule 7,

$$\mathscr{L}\{F^{(n)}(t)\} = s^n f(s) - s^{n-1}F(0+) - s^{n-2}F'(0+) - \ldots,$$
$$- sF^{(n-2)}(0+) - F^{(n-1)}(0+)$$

If $F^{(r)}(t)$ is also continuous at $t = 0$ for each $r = 0, 1, \ldots, n-1$, then $F^{(r)}(0+) = F^{(r)}(0)$ so that in this case,

$$\mathscr{L}\{F^{(n)}(t)\} = s^n f(s) - s^{n-1}F(0) - s^{n-2}F'(0), - \ldots, - sF^{(n-2)}(0) - F^{(n-1)}(0)$$

Rule 9   *Final s-Limit Rule*   The *first final s-limit* result states that

$$\lim_{s \to \infty} f(s) = 0 \text{ when } F(t) \in \text{class } \mathscr{A}$$

This follows from the corollary on page 4.

The *second final s-limit* results follows from Rule 7, for with the conditions of that rule we have, on applying the corollary to $F'(t)$,

$$\lim_{s \to \infty} \mathscr{L}\{F'(t)\} = \lim_{s \to \infty} [s\,f(s) - F(0+)] = 0$$

i.e. $\lim_{s \to \infty} s\,f(s) = F(0+)$, when the limit exists.

We can further construct higher order limit results, for example $\lim_{s \to \infty} s^n f(s)$ by using Rule 8.

Rule 10   Zero s-Limit Rule   Restricting $F(t)$ to *zero* exponential order as $t \to \infty$, i.e. $\lim_{t \to \infty} F(t) =$ constant, we have the *zero s-limit rule*,

$$\lim_{s \to 0+} s f(s) = \lim_{t \to \infty} F(t).$$

This is obtained as follows:

$$\lim_{T \to \infty} \lim_{s \to 0+} \int_0^T e^{-st} F'(t)\, dt = \lim_{T \to \infty} \int_0^T F'(t)\, dt = \lim_{T \to \infty} F(T) - F(0+)$$

However by Rule 7 since $\sigma = 0$, the left hand side equals
$\lim_{s \to 0+} s f(s) - F(0+)$

and so

$$\lim_{s \to 0+} s f(s) = \lim_{t \to \infty} F(t)$$

Problem 1.19   Evaluate $\mathscr{L}\{t^2 e^{pt}\}$ using the third order differential equation satisfied by $t^2 e^{pt}$.

Solution. The third order differential equation satisfied by $X(t) = t^2 e^{pt}$ is

$$(D - p)^3 X = 0 \qquad \text{where } D = d/dt$$

This follows from the result $D^n(e^{at} X) = (D + a)^n X$ when a is a constant and n any positive integer; it can be proved quite simply by using Liebniz' theorem. Choosing $a = -p$, $n = 3$ and $X = t^2 e^{pt}$, we have

$$(D - p)^3 (t^2 e^{pt}) = D^3(e^{-pt} t^2 e^{pt}) = D^3(t^2) = 0.$$

Alternatively, we have by successively differentiating $X(t) = t^2 e^{pt}$,

$$X' = pX + 2te^{pt}, \quad X'' = 2pX' - p^2 X + 2e^{pt}, \quad X''' = 2pX'' - p^2 X' + 2pe^{pt}$$

Eliminating e^{pt}, we get as before

$$X''' - 3pX'' + 3p^2 X' - p^3 X = 0 \tag{i}$$

Using Rule 8 with $n = 1, 2$ and 3 successively, and with $\mathscr{L}\{X(t)\} = x(s)$,

$$\mathscr{L}\{X'(t)\} = sx - X(0) = sx; \qquad \text{since } X(0) = 0$$

$$\mathscr{L}\{X''(t)\} = s^2 x - sX(0) - X'(0) = s^2 x, \qquad \text{since } X'(0) = 0$$

and

$$\mathscr{L}\{X'''(t)\} = s^3 x - s^2 X(0) - sX'(0) - X''(0) = s^3 x - 2 \qquad \text{since } X''(0) = 2.$$

18

Consequently, using the rule of addition and the differential equation (i)
$$\mathscr{L}\{X''' - 3pX'' + 3p^2X' - p^3X\} = 0 = s^3x - 2 - 3p(s^2x) + 3p^2(sx) - p^3x$$
i.e.
$$x(s^3 - 3ps^2 + 3p^2s - p^3) = 2,$$
or
$$x = \mathscr{L}\{t^2e^{pt}\} = 2/(s-p)^3 \qquad \square$$

Problem 1.20 Given that the Bessel functions of the first kind and positive integral orders satisfy the recurrence relations, $J_1 = J_0'$, $J_{n+1} = J_{n-1} - 2J_n'$, $n \geqslant 1$, with $J_0(0) = 1$, $J_n(0) = 0$, $n > 0$, show that
$$\mathscr{L}\{J_n(t)\} = [\sqrt{(s^2+1)} - s]^n / \sqrt{(s^2+1)}.$$

Solution. From Rule 7 and the first recurrence relation, we have
$$f_1 = \mathscr{L}\{J_1(t)\} = -\mathscr{L}\{J_0'(t)\} = -s\,f_0 + J_0(0)$$
But from Problem 1.10 $f_0 = \mathscr{L}\{J_0(t)\} = 1/\sqrt{(s^2+1)}$, so that the formula is true for $n = 0$. Also,
$$f_1 = \mathscr{L}\{J_1\} - -s(s^2 + 1)^{-\frac{1}{2}} + 1 - \frac{[\sqrt{(s^2+1)} - s]}{\sqrt{(s^2+1)}}$$
so that the formula is true for $n = 1$. From the second recurrence relation with $n = 1$ and $J'(0) = 0$,
$$f_2 = \mathscr{L}\{J_2\} = \mathscr{L}\{J_0\} - 2\mathscr{L}\{J_1'\} = f_0 - 2sf_1$$
$$= \frac{1}{\sqrt{(s^2+1)}} - \frac{2s(\sqrt{(s^2+1)} - s)}{\sqrt{(s^2+1)}} = \frac{(\sqrt{(s^2+1)} - s)^2}{\sqrt{(s^2+1)}}$$
i.e. the formula is true for $n = 2$. We now deduce the result for f_{n+1} assuming the validity of the formula for f_{n-1} and f_n, for they are certainly true when $n = 1$ and 2. Using the general recurrence relation for $n \geqslant 1$ with $J_n(0) = 0$,
$$f_{n+1} = \mathscr{L}\{J_{n+1}\} = \mathscr{L}\{J_{n-1}\} - 2s\,\mathscr{L}\{J_n\}$$
$$= \frac{[\sqrt{(s^2+1)} - s]^{n-1}}{\sqrt{(s^2+1)}} - \frac{2s[\sqrt{(s^2+1)} - s]^n}{\sqrt{(s^2+1)}}$$
$$= \frac{[\sqrt{(s^2+1)} - s]^{n-1}}{\sqrt{(s^2+1)}}[1 - 2s\sqrt{(s^2+1)} + 2s^2] = \frac{[\sqrt{(s^2+1)} - s]^{n+1}}{\sqrt{(s^2+1)}}$$
The result is true for $n = k+1$ if it is true for $n = k$ and $n = k-1$ so that the general result follows by induction. Moreover, using the rule of scale in Rule 2 we can deduce that
$$\mathscr{L}\{J_n(at)\} = \frac{(\sqrt{(s^2+a^2)} - s)^n}{a^n\sqrt{(s^2+a^2)}}, \qquad a > 0, n \geqslant 0 \qquad \square$$

Problem 1.21 Find the Laplace transform of $t^m L_n^m(t)$, where $L_n^m(t)$ is the Laguerre polynomial of degree n and order m (both integers) defined by $L_n^m(t) = t^{-m} e^t D^n (e^{-t} t^{n+m})/n!$ where $D \equiv d/dt$. Write down this polynomial by inverting its Laplace transform. (The Laguerre polynomial is a solution of the differential equation $tX'' + (m+1-t)X' + nX = 0$). What is the Laplace transform of $L_n^m(t)$?

Solution. Writing $n! t^n L_n^m(t) = X$ we have

$$\mathcal{L}\{e^{-t} X\} = \mathcal{L}\{D^n(e^{-t} t^{n+m})\} = s^n \mathcal{L}\{e^{-t} t^{n+m}\}$$

from Rule 8 where $F(t) = e^{-t} t^{n+m}$, so that
$F(0) = 0 = F'(0) \dots = F^{(n+1)}(0)$. Applying the theorem of shift (Rule 3) to $\mathcal{L}\{t^{n+m}\} = (n+m)! s^{-n-m-1}, s > 0$ we have

$$\mathcal{L}\{e^{-t} t^{n+m}\} = (n+m)!(s+1)^{-n-m-1} \qquad s > 1$$

i.e. $\mathcal{L}\{e^{-t} X\} = (n+m)! s^n (s+1)^{-n-m-1}$

whereupon, using Rule 3 again we get the required result

$$\mathcal{L}\{t^m L_n^m(t)\} = (n+m)!(s-1)^n s^{-n-m-1}/n! \qquad s > 0$$

To find the polynomial we have, after expanding the right hand side using the binomial theorem,

$$\mathcal{L}\{t^m L_n^m(t)\} = \frac{(n+m)!}{n!}\left(\frac{1}{s^{m+1}} - \frac{c_1}{s^{m+2}} + \frac{c_2}{s^{m+3}} - \dots + (-1)^n \frac{c_n}{s^{n+m+1}} \right)$$

where $c_r = n!/[r!(n-r)!]$. Since $\mathcal{L}\{t^r\} = r! s^{-r-1}$ the inversion of this latter Laplace transform is simply

$$t^m L_n^m(t) = \frac{(n+m)!}{n!}\left(\frac{t^n}{m!} - \frac{c_1 t^{m+1}}{(m+1)!} + \frac{c_2 t^{m+2}}{(m+2)!} - \dots + \frac{(-1^n c_n t^{m+n}}{(m+n)!} \right),$$

$$L_n^m(t) = \sum_{r=0}^{n} (-1)^r \frac{(n+m)!}{(n-r)!(m+r)!} \frac{t^r}{r!}$$

The Laplace transform of $L_n^m(t)$ by appeal to Rule 5 is
$[(n+m)!/n!][(-\mathcal{D})^m[(s-1)^n s^{-n-m-1}]$, $\mathcal{D} \equiv d/ds$ □

1.7 Laplace Transforms of Integrals
Rule 11   We have

$$\mathcal{L}\{e^{-at} \int_0^t e^{ax} F(x)\, dx\} = f(s)/(s+a)$$

where $\mathcal{L}\{F(t)\} = f(s), s > \sigma$ for, integrating by parts with respect to t,

$$\int_0^\infty e^{-(s+a)t} \left(\int_0^t e^{ax} F(x)\, dx \right) dt = (s+a)^{-1} \int_0^\infty e^{-st} F(t)\, dt$$

and the result follows. In particular when $a=0$

$$\mathcal{L}\left\{\int_0^t F(x)\,dx\right\} = s^{-1}f(s)$$

Problem 1.22 Prove that $\mathcal{L}\{e^t\operatorname{erfc} t^{\frac12}\} = 1/(s+\sqrt{s})$ where $\operatorname{erfc} t = 2\pi^{-\frac12}\int_t^\infty e^{-x^2}\,dx$.

Solution. We have

$$\operatorname{erfc} t = 2\pi^{-\frac12}\int_t^\infty e^{-x^2}\,dx = 2\pi^{-\frac12}\left[\int_0^\infty e^{-x^2}\,dx - \int_0^t e^{-x^2}\,dx\right]$$

Since $\int_0^\infty e^{-x^2}\,dx = \frac12\sqrt{\pi}$ and $2\pi^{-\frac12}\int_0^t e^{-x^2}\,dx = \operatorname{erf} t$ therefore

$$\operatorname{erfc} t = 1 - \operatorname{erf} t$$

(erf t is called the *error function* of t and erfc t is its *complement*.)

$$\mathcal{L}\{\operatorname{erfc} t^{\frac12}\} = \mathcal{L}\{1\} - \mathcal{L}\{\operatorname{erf} t^{\frac12}\}$$

$$= s^{-1} - \mathcal{L}\left\{2\pi^{-\frac12}\int_0^{\sqrt t} e^{-x^2}\,dx\right\}$$

$$= s^{-1} - \mathcal{L}\left\{\pi^{-\frac12}\int_0^t e^{-v}v^{-\frac12}\,dv\right\}\quad (v=x^2)\qquad\text{(i)}$$

Using Rule 3 and Problem 1.5, $\mathcal{L}\{e^{-t}/\sqrt t\} = f(s+1)$ where $f(s) = \mathcal{L}\{1/\sqrt t\} = \sqrt{(\pi/s)}$. Hence

By Rule 11,
$$\mathcal{L}\left\{\frac{e^{-t}}{\sqrt t}\right\} = \sqrt{\left[\frac{\pi}{(s+1)}\right]}$$

$$\mathcal{L}\left\{\int_0^t e^{-v}\frac{dv}{\sqrt v}\right\} = \frac1s\sqrt{\left(\frac{\pi}{s+1}\right)}$$

Therefore, from (i),

$$\mathcal{L}\{\operatorname{erfc} t^{\frac12}\} = \frac1s\left(1 - \frac{1}{\sqrt{(s+1)}}\right) = \frac{\sqrt{(s+1)}-1}{s\sqrt{(s+1)}} = \frac{1}{\sqrt{(s+1)}[\sqrt{(s+1)}+1]}$$

By Rule 3,
$$\mathcal{L}\{e^t\operatorname{erfc} t^{\frac12}\} = \frac{1}{[\sqrt{s}(\sqrt s+1)]} = \frac{1}{(s+\sqrt s)}$$

Problem 1.23 Find $\mathcal{L}\left\{\int_0^t [(e^{ax}-\cos bx)/x]\,dx\right\}$ and deduce that

$$\mathcal{L}\left\{\int_0^t \frac{\sin^2 x}{x}\,dx\right\} = \frac{1}{2s}\ln\left(\frac{\sqrt{(s^2+4)}}{s-1}\right)$$

Solution. We have

$$\mathcal{L}\{e^{at}-\cos bt\} = \frac{1}{s-a} - \frac{s}{s^2+b^2},\qquad s>a$$

$$\lim_{t\to 0}[(e^{at}-\cos bt)/t] = a$$

21

so that by Rule 6,

$$\mathscr{L}\left\{\frac{e^{at}-\cos bt}{t}\right\} = \int_s^\infty \left(\frac{1}{x-a}-\frac{x}{x^2+b^2}\right)dx$$

$$= [\ln(x-a)-\tfrac{1}{2}\ln(x^2+b^2)]_s^\infty$$

$$= \ln(\sqrt{(s^2+b^2)}/(s-a))$$

since $\lim\limits_{x\to\infty} \ln(\sqrt{(x^2+b^2)}/(x-a)) = \ln 1 = 0$. Finally, using Rule 11,

$$\mathscr{L}\left\{\int_0^t \frac{e^{ax}-\cos bx}{x}dx\right\} = \frac{1}{s}\ln\left(\frac{\sqrt{(s^2+b^2)}}{s-a}\right), \qquad s > a$$

Putting $a = 1, b = 2, (e^{ax}-\cos bx)/x = (1-\cos 2x)/x = (2\sin^2 x)/x$.
Hence

$$\mathscr{L}\left\{\int_0^t \frac{\sin^2 x}{x}dx\right\} = \frac{1}{2s}\ln\left(\frac{\sqrt{(s^2+4)}}{s-1}\right) \qquad s > 1. \qquad \square$$

1.8 Laplace Transforms via Differential Equations So far we have determined Laplace transforms by using the fundamental definition or some variant of it involving, e.g. recurrence relations, complex values, term-by-term integration. Moreover, we have shown how Laplace transforms may be generated through the use of the various operational rules. Another method involves finding a differential equation satisfied by the transform $f(s)$ and solving it. In some instances when f is regarded as a function of some parameter α so that $f = f(s\,\alpha)$ we find a differential equation with α as independent variable and solve this. The next three problems illustrate the method.

Problem 1.24 Find $\mathscr{L}\{L_n(t)\}$ where $L_n(t)$ is the polynomial solution of the differential equation $tX''+(1-t)X'+nX = 0$ such that $L_n(0) = 1$, $L_n'(0) = -n$.

Solution. This question has already been considered in Problem 1.21 with $m \neq 0$. Here we give a different solution based on Rule 5. We write

$$L_n(t) = X, \qquad \mathscr{L}\{L_n(t)\} = x(s)$$

Since $tX''+(1-t)X'+nX = 0$, then $\mathscr{L}\{tX''+(1-t)X'+nX\} = 0$
Now, applying Rules 5 and 8 with $\mathscr{D} \equiv d/ds$ we have,

$$\mathscr{L}\{X'\} = sx-L_n(0) = sx-1$$

$$\mathscr{L}\{X''\} = s^2x-sL_n(0)-L_n'(0) = s^2x-s+n$$

$$\mathscr{L}\{tX'\} = -\mathscr{D}\mathscr{L}\{X'\} = -\mathscr{D}(sx-1)$$

$$\mathscr{L}\{tX''\} = -\mathscr{D}\mathscr{L}\{X''\} = -\mathscr{D}(s^2x-s+n)$$

Hence

$$-\mathscr{D}(s^2x-s+n)+(1+\mathscr{D})(sx-1)+nx = 0$$
$$s(1-s)\mathscr{D}x+(n-s+1)x = 0$$

$$\frac{1}{x}\frac{dx}{ds}+\frac{n+1}{s}+\frac{n}{1-s} = 0$$

Integrating, we obtain

$$\ln x+(n+1)\ln s-n\ln(1-s) = \text{constant} = \ln A$$

so that $x = As^{-n-1}(1-s)^n$. The constant A may now be evaluated by the second final s-limit theorem of Rule 9 in which
$\lim\limits_{s\to\infty} sx(s) = (-1)^n A = X(0+) = L_n(0) = 1$. Hence

$$\mathscr{L}\{L_n(t)\} = x = s^{-n-1}(s-1)^n$$

Its inversion, if desired, can be accomplished using the method of Problem 1.21. $\qquad\blacksquare$

Problem 1.25 Evaluate $\mathscr{L}\{\sin at^{\frac12}\}$ and $\mathscr{L}\{t^{-\frac12}\cos at^{\frac12}\}$ by finding a differential equation satisfied by the first transform.

Solution. We write $\sin at^{\frac12} = F(t)$, $\mathscr{L}\{\sin at^{\frac12}\} = f(s)$, $s > 0$. Using Rule 7
$$\mathscr{L}\{F'(t)\} = \mathscr{L}\{\tfrac12 at^{-\frac12}\cos at^{\frac12}\} = sf(s) \qquad (F(0) = 0) \qquad \text{(i)}$$
$$= \int_0^\infty e^{-st}\tfrac12 at^{-\frac12}\cos at\ = a\int_0^\infty e^{-st}\cos at^{\frac12}\,d(t^{\frac12})$$
$$= a[e^{-st}t^{\frac12}\cos at^{\frac12}]_0^\infty - a\int_0^\infty t^{\frac12}\,d(e^{-st}\cos at^{\frac12})$$
$$= 0-a\int_0^\infty(-se^{-st}t^{\frac12}\cos at^{\frac12}-\tfrac12 ae^{-st}\sin at^{\frac12})\,dt$$
$$= -s\frac{d}{ds}(2sf)+\tfrac12 a^2 f,$$

where (i) and Rule 5 have been used in the first integral. Hence

$$sf = -2s\left(s\frac{df}{ds}+f\right)+\tfrac12 a^2 f \quad\text{or}\quad \frac{1}{f}\frac{df}{ds} = -\frac{3}{2s}+\frac{a^2}{4s^2}$$

Integrating,

$$\ln f = -\tfrac32\ln s-\frac{a^2}{4s}+\ln A \qquad (A = \text{constant})$$

i.e. $\qquad f = As^{-\frac32}e^{-a^2/4s} = \mathscr{L}\{\sin at^{\frac12}\}, \qquad s > 0$

Also $\qquad \mathscr{L}\{t^{-\frac12}\cos at^{\frac12}\} = 2sf/a = Bs^{-\frac12}e^{-a^2/4s}$

where $B = A/a$.

We can find B by putting $a = 0$, for using the result of Problem 1.5 we have $\mathscr{L}\{t^{-\frac{1}{2}}\} = (\pi/s)^{\frac{1}{2}} = Bs^{-\frac{1}{2}}$ which gives $B = \pi^{\frac{1}{2}}$. Hence $A = a\pi^{\frac{1}{2}}$ and

$$\mathscr{L}\{\sin at^{\frac{1}{2}}\} = \tfrac{1}{2}a(\pi/s^3)^{\frac{1}{2}}e^{-a^2/4s} \qquad \mathscr{L}\{t^{-\frac{1}{2}}\cos at^{\frac{1}{2}}\} = (\pi/s)^{\frac{1}{2}}e^{-a^2/4s}$$

Alternative Solution. Another method entails finding the differential equation satisfied by the function $F(t) = \sin at^{\frac{1}{2}}$.

Differentiating, we find

$$F'(t) = \tfrac{1}{2}at^{-\frac{1}{2}}\cos at^{\frac{1}{2}} \quad \text{or} \quad 2t^{\frac{1}{2}}F' = a\cos at^{\frac{1}{2}}$$

where a prime denotes differentiation with respect to t. Differentiating both sides, we have

$$2t^{\frac{1}{2}}F'' + t^{-\frac{1}{2}}F' = -\tfrac{1}{2}a^2t^{-\frac{1}{2}}\sin at^{\frac{1}{2}}$$

Eliminating $\sin at^{\frac{1}{2}}$ we find the required differential equation satisfied by F to be $4tF'' + 2F' + a^2F = 0$. Taking the transform,

$$-4\,(d/ds)[s^2f - s\,F(0) - F'(0)] + 2[sf - F(0)] + a^2f = 0$$

and since $F(0) = 0$ and $F'(0)$ is eliminated by differentiation,

$$4s^2\frac{df}{ds} + (6s - a^2)f = 0, \qquad \text{i.e.} \frac{1}{f}\frac{df}{ds} = -\frac{3}{2s} + \frac{a^2}{4s}$$

as before. □

Problem 1.26 The Bessel function $J_0(x)$ of the first kind and zero order is a solution of the differential equation $xY'' + Y' + xY = 0$, and for small x, $J_0(x)$ is approximately unity. Deduce that $\mathscr{L}\{J_0(\alpha t^{\frac{1}{2}})\} = e^{-\alpha^2/4s}/s$, $\alpha > 0$, $s > 0$.

Solution. Here we illustrate the method in which a differential equation is constructed for the transform regarded as a function of the parameter α. We write

$$\phi(\alpha) = \int_0^\infty e^{-st}J_0(\alpha t^{\frac{1}{2}})\,dt \equiv \mathscr{L}\{J_0(\alpha t^{\frac{1}{2}})\}$$

Using primes to denote *total* differentials, so that $\phi'(\alpha) \equiv d\phi/d\alpha$, $J_0'(u) \equiv dJ_0/du$, we have, on differentiating successively with respect to α (note the parameter s will be regarded as constant in this solution for, strictly, ϕ is also a function of s),

$$\phi'(\alpha) = \mathscr{L}\{t^{\frac{1}{2}}J_0'(\alpha t^{\frac{1}{2}})\}, \qquad \phi''(\alpha) = \mathscr{L}\{tJ_0''(\alpha t^{\frac{1}{2}})\}.$$

However, $xJ_0''(x) + J_0'(x) + x\,J_0(x) = 0$ or, putting $x = \alpha t^{\frac{1}{2}}$,

$$\alpha t^{\frac{1}{2}}J_0''(\alpha t^{\frac{1}{2}}) + J_0'(\alpha t^{\frac{1}{2}}) + \alpha t^{\frac{1}{2}}J_0(\alpha t^{\frac{1}{2}}) = 0$$

Multiplying by $t^{\frac{1}{2}}$ and taking the transform,

$$\alpha\,\phi''(\alpha) + \phi'(\alpha) + \alpha\mathscr{L}\{t\,J_0(\alpha t^{\frac{1}{2}})\} = 0$$

We can express this latter transform in terms of $\phi(\alpha)$ and $\phi'(\alpha)$ on integrating by parts, i.e.

$$\int_0^\infty e^{-st} t\, J_0(\alpha t^{\frac{1}{2}})\, dt = \left[-\frac{1}{s} e^{-st} t\, J_0(\alpha t^{\frac{1}{2}}) \right]_0^\infty + \frac{1}{s} \int_0^\infty e^{-st} d[t\, J_0(\alpha t^{\frac{1}{2}})]$$

$$= \frac{1}{s} \int_0^\infty e^{-st}\left[J_0(\alpha t^{\frac{1}{2}}) + \tfrac{1}{2}\alpha t^{\frac{1}{2}} J_0'(\alpha t^{\frac{1}{2}}) \right] dt$$

$$= \frac{1}{s}\phi(\alpha) + \frac{\alpha}{2s}\phi'(\alpha)$$

The required equation is

$$\alpha\phi''(\alpha) + \phi'(\alpha) + \left(\frac{\alpha}{s}\right)\phi(\alpha) + \left(\frac{\alpha^2}{2s}\right)\phi'(\alpha) = 0$$

or
$$\alpha(2s\phi'' + \alpha\phi' + \phi) + (2s\phi' + \alpha\phi) = 0$$

To solve, put $2s\phi' + \alpha\phi = u$ so that $u' = 2s\phi'' + \alpha\phi' + \phi$. Hence,

$$\alpha u' + u = 0 = (d/d\alpha)(u\alpha)$$

Integrating, $u = A/\alpha = 2s\phi' + \alpha\phi$ where $A = $ constant. An integrating factor of this differential equation is $e^{\alpha^2/4s}$. Hence,

$$2s(d/d\alpha)(\phi e^{\alpha^2/4s}) = (A/\alpha)e^{\alpha^2/4s}$$

Integrating

$$2s\phi = e^{-\alpha^2/4s} \int (A/\alpha)e^{\alpha^2/4s} d\alpha + B e^{-\alpha^2/4s}.$$

The first term on the right hand side is infinite as $\alpha \to 0$, so that $A = 0$.
Since $J_0(\alpha t^{\frac{1}{2}})$ behaves like 1 for small α, we have

$$\phi(\alpha) = \int_0^\infty e^{-st} \cdot 1\, dt = \frac{1}{s}$$

so that $B = 2$, and finally $\phi(\alpha) = e^{-\alpha^2/4s}/s$. □

Alternatively we could use the second final s-limit Rule 9 to find B, for

$$\lim_{s \to \infty} s\phi = J_0(0) = 1 = \tfrac{1}{2}B.$$

1.9 Miscellaneous Functions
The Gamma Function The *gamma function* $\Gamma(x)$ is defined by

$$\Gamma(x+1) = \int_0^\infty t^x e^{-t}\, dt \qquad \text{for } x > -1.$$

When $x > 0$,

$$\int_0^\infty t^x e^{-t}\, dt = x \int_0^\infty t^{x-1} e^{-t}\, dt \qquad \text{i.e. } \Gamma(x+1) = x\Gamma(x).$$

Since $\Gamma(1) = \int_0^\infty e^{-t} dt = 1$, repeated application of the last formula gives $\Gamma(n+1) = n!$ where $n = 0, 1, 2, \ldots$. Again, by Problem 1.5, $\Gamma(\frac{1}{2}) = \int_0^\infty t^{-\frac{1}{2}} e^{-t} dt = \sqrt{\pi}$. It follows that

$$\mathscr{L}\{t^x\} = \int_0^\infty e^{-st}t^x \, dt = \int_0^\infty e^{-t}\left(\frac{t}{s}\right)^x \frac{dt}{s} = \frac{\Gamma(x+1)}{s^{x+1}}, \qquad x > -1, s > 0$$

Putting $x = n$, $\mathscr{L}\{t^n\} = n! \, s^{-n-1}$; putting $x = n+\frac{1}{2}$,

$$\mathscr{L}\{t^{n+\frac{1}{2}}\} = \Gamma(n+\frac{3}{2})s^{-n-\frac{3}{2}} = (n+\frac{1}{2})(n-\frac{1}{2})(n-\frac{3}{2})\ldots\frac{1}{2}\sqrt{\pi}s^{-n-\frac{3}{2}}$$

Problem 1.27 Evaluate $\mathscr{L}\{\ln t\}$.

Solution. Differentiating with respect to x the defining formula $\Gamma(x+1) = \int_0^\infty u^x e^{-u} du$ gives

$$\Gamma'(x+1) = \int_0^\infty u^x \ln u \, e^{-u} du$$

Putting $x = 0$,

$$\Gamma'(1) = \int_0^\infty e^{-u}\ln u \, du = s\int_0^\infty e^{-st}\ln(st) \, dt$$

$$= s\ln s \int_0^\infty e^{-st} dt + s\int_0^\infty e^{-st}\ln t \, dt = \ln s + s\mathscr{L}\{\ln t\}$$

Hence therefore,

$$\mathscr{L}\{\ln t\} = [\Gamma'(1) - \ln s]/s \qquad \square$$

Periodic Functions Given $F(t)$ is a periodic function with period τ and is piecewise continuous in $0 < t < \tau$, we have $\mathscr{L}\{F(t)\} = f_\tau(s)/(1 - e^{-\tau s})$, $s > 0$, where $f_\tau(s) = \int_0^\tau e^{-st}F(t) \, dt$

Proof. $\mathscr{L}\{F(t)\} = \int_0^\infty e^{-st}F(t) \, dt = \displaystyle\sum_{n=0}^\infty \int_{n\tau}^{(n+1)\tau} e^{-st}F(t) \, dt.$

Let $x = t - n\tau$, then

$$\mathscr{L}\{F(t)\} = \sum_{n=0}^\infty e^{-n\tau s} \int_0^\tau e^{-sx}F(x+n\tau) \, dx = \left(\int_0^\tau e^{-sx}F(x) \, dx\right)\sum_{n=0}^\infty e^{-n\tau s}$$

since $F(x+n\tau) = F(x)$ by the periodicity of $F(t)$. Because the integral is independent of n, this change of order of summation is permissible. Also for $s > 0$, $e^{-n\tau s} < 1$ so that $\displaystyle\sum_{n=0}^\infty e^{-n\tau s} = 1/(1 - e^{-\tau s})$, and the result follows.

Problem 1.28 Given the parabolic wave function $P(t)$ defined by

26

$$P(t) = \begin{cases} t(1-t) & 0 \leqslant t \leqslant 1 \\ (t-1)(t-2) & 1 \leqslant t \leqslant 2 \end{cases}$$

$$P(t+2) = P(t)$$

find $\mathscr{L}\{F(t)\}$ where (i) $F(t)$ is the half-wave rectification of $P(t)$, (ii) $F(t)$ is the full-wave rectification of $P(t)$.

Solution (i) The half-wave rectification function $F(t)$ is defined by

$$F(t) = \tfrac{1}{2}\{P(t) + |P(t)|\} = \begin{cases} t(1-t) & 0 \leqslant t \leqslant 1 \\ 0 & 1 \leqslant t \leqslant 2 \end{cases}$$

i.e. the negative part of $F(t)$ is cancelled also $F(t+2) = F(t)$, i.e. $F(t)$ is periodic with period $\tau = 2$. Hence

$$(1 - e^{-2s})\mathscr{L}\{F(t) = \int_0^2 e^{-sx} F(x)\, dx = \int_0^1 e^{-sx} x(1-x)\, dx$$

$$= [e^{-sx} s^{-3}(2 + 2xs - s + x^2 s^2 - xs)]_0^1$$

$$= s^{-3}\{(2+s)e^{-s} - 2 + s\}$$

giving

$$\mathscr{L}\{F(t)\} = \frac{1}{s^2(1-e^{-s})} - \frac{2}{s^3(1+e^{-s})}$$

(ii) The full-wave rectification $F(t)$ is defined by

$$F(t) = |P(t)| = \begin{cases} t(1-t) & 0 \leqslant t \leqslant 1 \\ (t-1)(2-t) & 1 \leqslant t \leqslant 2 \end{cases}$$

with $F(t)$ periodic and $\tau = 2$. Hence

$$(1-e^{-2s})\mathscr{L}\{F(t)\} = \int_0^2 e^{-sx} F(x)\, dx = \int_0^1 e^{-sx} x(1-x)\, dx$$

$$+ \int_1^2 e^{-sx}(x-1)(2-x)\, dx$$

$$= \int_0^1 e^{-sx} x(1-x)\, dx$$

$$+ \int_0^1 e^{-s-su} u(1-u)\, du \qquad x = 1+u$$

$$= (1+e^{-s}) \int_0^1 e^{-sx} x(1-x)\, dx$$

Using the result in (1),

$$\mathscr{L}\{F(t)\} = \frac{1+e^{-s}}{s^2(1-e^{-s})} - \frac{2}{s^3}$$

$$= s^{-2}\coth\tfrac{1}{2}s - 2s^{-3} \qquad\qquad \square$$

EXERCISES

Evaluate the Laplace transforms of:

1. $\sin^3 pt,\ \sin^4 pt,\ \cos^3 pt,\ \cos^4 pt.$

2. $e^{\frac{1}{2}at}\{\sqrt{3}\sin\frac{1}{2}\sqrt{3}at - \cos\frac{1}{2}\sqrt{3}at + e^{-3at/2}\}.$

3. $I_n(at), n > 1.$

4. $2(\cos at - \cos bt)/t.$

5. $J_0(a\sqrt{(t^2 + 2bt)}),\ t^{\frac{1}{2}n}J_n(at^{\frac{1}{2}}), a > 0.$

6. $t^n \ln t, n > -1.$

7. $\{\pi(t+a)\}^{-\frac{1}{2}}.$

8. $F(t) = \begin{cases} \sin \pi t/a & 0 \leqslant t \leqslant a \\ 0 & t > a \end{cases}$

Chapter 2

Inversion of the Laplace Transform

2.1 The Inverse Given a function $F(t)$ with $\mathscr{L}\{F(t)\} = f(s)$, we define $F(t)$ as the *inverse* Laplace transform of $f(s)$ and write

$$\mathscr{L}^{-1}\{f(s)\} = F(t)$$

where $\mathscr{L}^{-1}$ is the inverse operator of the Laplace transform i.e. it restores the Laplace transform to the original function. Examples are,

$$\mathscr{L}^{-1}\left\{\frac{a}{s^2+a^2}\right\} = \sin at, \qquad \mathscr{L}^{-1}\left\{\frac{s}{s^2+a^2}\right\} = \cos at$$

$$\mathscr{L}^{-1}\left\{\frac{a}{s^2-a^2}\right\} = \sinh at, \qquad \mathscr{L}^{-1}\left\{\frac{s}{s^2-a^2}\right\} = \cosh at$$

$$\mathscr{L}^{-1}\{s^{-n-1}\} = t^n/\Gamma(n+1)$$

2.2 Null Functions and Uniqueness We define a *null function* $N(t)$ as one for which $\int_0^T N(t)\,dt = 0$ for all positive T. A null function cannot be a continuous function unless it vanishes for all $t \geqslant 0$.

A theorem due to Lerch states that if

$$\mathscr{L}\{F(t)\} = f(s) = \mathscr{L}\{G(t)\}$$

then
$$F(t) - G(t) = N(t)$$

Consequently, given $f(s)$ for which we find a *continuous* inverse $F(t)$ over a given closed interval, this function is *the unique continuous solution* for the inverse over that interval.

2.3 Operational Rules of Inverse Laplace Transforms These correspond exactly to some of the properties of the original transforms listed under the rule numbers of Chapter 1. We therefore use the same numbers for corresponding rules.

Rule 1 Rule of Addition Given $\mathscr{L}^{-1}\{f_1(s)\} = F_1(t)$,
$\mathscr{L}^{-1}\{f_2(s)\} = F_2(t), \ldots, \mathscr{L}^{-1}\{f_n(s)\} = F_n(t)$ and any constants $a_1, a_2, \ldots, a_n$, we have

$$\mathscr{L}^{-1}\{a_1 f_1(s) + a_2 f_2(s) + \ldots + a_n f_n(s)\}$$
$$= a_1 F_1(t) + a_2 F_2(t) + \ldots + a_n F_n(t)$$

Problem 2.1 Evaluate (a) $\mathscr{L}^{-1}\{(2s+3)/(s^2+4)\}$, (b) $\mathscr{L}^{-1}\{(\sqrt{s}-2)^3/s^4\}$.

Solution.

(a) $\mathcal{L}^{-1}\left\{\dfrac{2s+3}{s^2+4}\right\} = \mathcal{L}^{-1}\left\{\dfrac{2s}{s^2+4}+\dfrac{3}{s^2+4}\right\}$

$\qquad\qquad\qquad = 2\mathcal{L}^{-1}\left\{\dfrac{s}{s^2+4}\right\}+\dfrac{3}{2}\mathcal{L}^{-1}\left\{\dfrac{2}{s^2+4}\right\}$

$\qquad\qquad\qquad = 2\cos 2t+\tfrac{3}{2}\sin 2t$

(b) $\mathcal{L}^{-1}\left\{\dfrac{((\sqrt{s}-2)^3)}{s^4}\right\} = \mathcal{L}^{-1}\left\{\dfrac{s^{\frac{3}{2}}-6s+12s^{\frac{1}{2}}-8}{s^4}\right\}$

$\qquad\qquad\qquad = \mathcal{L}^{-1}\left\{\dfrac{1}{s^{\frac{5}{2}}}-\dfrac{6}{s^3}+\dfrac{12}{s^{\frac{7}{2}}}-\dfrac{8}{s^4}\right\}$

$\qquad\qquad\qquad = \dfrac{t^{\frac{3}{2}}}{\Gamma(\frac{5}{2})}-\dfrac{6t^2}{\Gamma(3)}+\dfrac{12t^{\frac{5}{2}}}{\Gamma(\frac{7}{2})}-\dfrac{8t^3}{\Gamma(4)}$

which, using $\Gamma(n+1) = n\,\Gamma(n)$, with $\Gamma(1) = 1$, $\Gamma(\frac{1}{2}) = \pi^{\frac{1}{2}}$, becomes

$$\dfrac{4t^{\frac{3}{2}}}{3\pi^{\frac{1}{2}}}-3t^2+\dfrac{32t^{\frac{5}{2}}}{5\pi^{\frac{1}{2}}}-\dfrac{4t^3}{3} \qquad\qquad \square$$

Rule 2 Rule of Scale   Given $a > 0$ with $\mathcal{L}^{-1}\{f(s)\} = F(t)$, then $\mathcal{L}^{-1}\{f(as)\} = a^{-1}F(t/a)$.

Problem 2.2   Evaluate $\mathcal{L}^{-1}\{(1-2s\sqrt{3})/(4s^2+1)\}$.

Solution. Since $\mathcal{L}^{-1}\{1/(s^2+1)\} = \sin t$, and $\mathcal{L}^{-1}\{s/(s^2+1)\} = \cos t$, we have $\mathcal{L}^{-1}\{1/(4s^2+1)\} = \tfrac{1}{2}\sin\tfrac{1}{2}t$ and $\mathcal{L}^{-1}\{2s/(4s^2+1)\} = \tfrac{1}{2}\cos\tfrac{1}{2}t$ by Rule 2. Hence using Rule 1,

$$\mathcal{L}^{-1}\left\{\dfrac{1-2s\sqrt{3}}{4s^2+1}\right\} = \mathcal{L}^{-1}\left\{\dfrac{1}{4s^2+1}\right\}-\sqrt{3}\mathcal{L}^{-1}\left\{\dfrac{2s}{4s^2+1}\right\}$$

$$= \dfrac{1}{2}\sin\tfrac{1}{2}t-\dfrac{\sqrt{3}}{2}\cos\tfrac{1}{2}t = \sin(\tfrac{1}{2}t-\tfrac{1}{3}\pi) \qquad\qquad \square$$

Rule 3 Rule of Shift in the Transformed Function   Given $\mathcal{L}^{-1}\{f(s)\} = F(t)$ we have $\mathcal{L}^{-1}\{f(s+\omega)\} = e^{-\omega t}F(t) = e^{-\omega t}\mathcal{L}^{-1}\{f(s)\}$.

Problem 2.3   Find the inverse transform of each of the following:

(a) $\dfrac{3s-5}{4s^2-4s+37}$ (b) $\dfrac{3s-5}{4s^2-4s+1}$ (c) $\dfrac{s^2}{(2s+3)^{\frac{5}{2}}}$ (d) $\dfrac{1}{\sqrt{(s^2+s+1)}}$.

Solution

(a) $\dfrac{3s-5}{4s^2-4s+37} = \dfrac{3s-5}{4[s-\frac{1}{2})^2+9]} = \dfrac{3(s-\frac{1}{2})-\frac{7}{2}}{4[(s-\frac{1}{2})^2+9]}$

Hence

$$\mathscr{L}^{-1}\left\{\frac{3s-5}{4s^2-4s+37}\right\} = \frac{3}{4}\mathscr{L}^{-1}\left\{\frac{s-\frac{1}{2}}{(s-\frac{1}{2})^2+3^2}\right\} - \frac{7}{24}\mathscr{L}^{-1}\left\{\frac{3}{(s-\frac{1}{2})^2+3^2}\right\}$$

$$= \tfrac{3}{4}e^{\frac{1}{2}t}\cos 3t - \tfrac{7}{24}e^{\frac{1}{2}t}\sin 3t = \tfrac{1}{24}e^{\frac{1}{2}t}(18\cos 3t - 7\sin 3t)$$

(b) $$\frac{3s-5}{4s^2+4s+1} = \frac{3s-5}{4(s+\frac{1}{2})^2} = \frac{3(s+\frac{1}{2})-\frac{13}{2}}{4(s+\frac{1}{2})^2}$$

Hence

$$\mathscr{L}^{-1}\left\{\frac{3s-5}{4s^2+4s+1}\right\} = \frac{3}{4}\mathscr{L}^{-1}\left\{\frac{1}{s+\frac{1}{2}}\right\} - \frac{13}{8}\mathscr{L}^{-1}\left\{\frac{1}{(s+\frac{1}{2})^2}\right\}$$

$$= \tfrac{3}{4}e^{-\frac{1}{2}t} - \tfrac{13}{8}e^{-\frac{1}{2}t}t = \tfrac{1}{8}e^{-\frac{1}{2}t}(6-13t)$$

(c) $s^2/(2s+3)^{\frac{5}{2}} = s^2/[2^{\frac{5}{2}}(s+\frac{3}{2})^{\frac{5}{2}}]$. If $u = s+\frac{3}{2}$, this becomes

$$\frac{(u-\frac{3}{2})^2}{2^{\frac{5}{2}}u^{\frac{5}{2}}} = \frac{u^2-3u+\frac{9}{4}}{2^{\frac{5}{2}}u^{\frac{5}{2}}} = \frac{1}{2^{\frac{5}{2}}}\left(\frac{1}{u^{\frac{1}{2}}} - \frac{3}{u^{\frac{3}{2}}} + \frac{9}{4u^{\frac{5}{2}}}\right)$$

Hence, by Rule 3, followed by the application of $\mathscr{L}^{-1}\{s^{-n-1}\} = t^n/\Gamma(n+1)$, $n > -1$,

$$\mathscr{L}^{-1}\left\{\frac{s^2}{(2s+3)^{\frac{5}{2}}}\right\} = \frac{1}{2^{\frac{5}{2}}}\mathscr{L}^{-1}\left\{\frac{1}{(s+\frac{3}{2})^{\frac{1}{2}}} - \frac{3}{(s+\frac{3}{2})^{\frac{3}{2}}} + \frac{9}{4(s+\frac{3}{2})^{\frac{5}{2}}}\right\}$$

$$= \frac{1}{2^{\frac{5}{2}}}e^{-\frac{3}{2}t}\mathscr{L}^{-1}\left\{\frac{1}{s^{\frac{1}{2}}} - \frac{3}{s^{\frac{3}{2}}} + \frac{9}{4s^{\frac{5}{2}}}\right\}$$

$$= \frac{1}{2^{\frac{5}{2}}}e^{-\frac{3}{2}t}\left(\frac{t^{-\frac{1}{2}}}{\Gamma(\frac{1}{2})} - \frac{3t^{\frac{1}{2}}}{\Gamma(\frac{3}{2})} + \frac{9t^{\frac{3}{2}}}{4\Gamma(\frac{5}{2})}\right)$$

$$= \frac{1}{2^{\frac{5}{2}}}e^{-\frac{3}{2}t}\left(\frac{t^{-\frac{1}{2}}}{\pi^{\frac{1}{2}}} - \frac{3t^{\frac{1}{2}}}{\frac{1}{2}\pi^{\frac{1}{2}}} + \frac{9t^{\frac{3}{2}}}{4\cdot\frac{3}{2}\cdot\frac{1}{2}\pi^{\frac{1}{2}}}\right)$$

$$= \frac{1}{\sqrt{(32\pi t)}}e^{-\frac{3}{2}t}(1-6t+3t^2)$$

(d) $$\mathscr{L}^{-1}\left\{\frac{1}{\sqrt{(s^2+s+1)}}\right\} = \mathscr{L}^{-1}\left\{\frac{1}{\sqrt{[(s+\frac{1}{2})^2+\frac{3}{4}]}}\right\}$$

$$= e^{-\frac{1}{2}t}\mathscr{L}^{-1}\left\{\frac{1}{\sqrt{(s^2+\frac{3}{4})}}\right\}$$

$$= e^{-\frac{1}{2}t}J_0(\tfrac{1}{2}\sqrt{3}t)$$

since $\mathscr{L}\{J_0(at)\} = 1/\sqrt{(s^2+a^2)}$. □

Problem 2.4 Find the inverse transform of $(As+B)/(s^2+2bs+c)$, where A, B, b and c are real constants.

31

Solution.

$$F(t) = \mathcal{L}^{-1}\left\{\frac{As+B}{s^2+2bs+c}\right\} = \mathcal{L}^{-1}\left\{\frac{A(s+b)+B-Ab}{(s+b)^2+c-b^2}\right\}$$

$$= e^{-bt}\mathcal{L}^{-1}\left\{\frac{As+B-Ab}{s^2+c-b^2}\right\}$$

We have three cases to consider according as $c >$, $=$, or $< b^2$.

Case (i) $c > b^2$. Put $\sqrt{(c-b^2)} = \alpha$ where α is real. Then

$$F(t) = e^{-bt}A\,\mathcal{L}^{-1}\left\{\frac{s}{s^2+\alpha^2}\right\}+e^{-bt}\frac{(B-Ab)}{\alpha}\,\mathcal{L}^{-1}\left\{\frac{\alpha}{s^2+\alpha^2}\right\}$$

$$= e^{-bt}\left(A\cos\alpha t+\frac{B-Ab}{\alpha}\sin\alpha t\right)$$

Case (ii) $c = b^2$.

$$F(t) = e^{-bt}\mathcal{L}^{-1}\left\{\frac{As+B-Ab}{s^2}\right\} = e^{-bt}A\,\mathcal{L}^{-1}\left\{\frac{1}{s}\right\}+e^{-bt}(B-Ab)\mathcal{L}^{-1}\left\{\frac{1}{s^2}\right\}$$

$$= e^{-bt}[A+(B-Ab)t].$$

Case (iii) $c < b^2$. Put $\sqrt{(b^2-c)} = \beta$, where β is real. Then

$$F(t) = e^{-bt}A\,\mathcal{L}^{-1}\left\{\frac{s}{s^2-\beta^2}\right\}+e^{-bt}\frac{(B-Ab)}{\beta}\,\mathcal{L}^{-1}\left\{\frac{\beta}{s^2-\beta^2}\right\}$$

$$= e^{-bt}\left(A\cosh\beta t+\frac{B-Ab}{\beta}\sinh\beta t\right)$$

or, alternatively, since $\cosh\beta t = \frac{1}{2}(e^{\beta t}+e^{-\beta t})$, $\sinh\beta t = \frac{1}{2}(e^{\beta t}-e^{-\beta t})$,

$$F(t) = [e^{(\beta-b)t}(A\beta+B-Ab)+e^{-(\beta+b)t}(A\beta-B+Ab)]/2\beta \qquad \square$$

Rule 4 Rule of Shift in the Original Function Given $\mathcal{L}^{-1}\{f(s)\} = F(t)$, then for $\tau > 0$

$$\mathcal{L}^{-1}\{e^{-s\tau}f(s)\} = H(t-\tau)F(t-\tau)$$

where $H(t-\tau) = 0$ if $t \leqslant \tau$, and $H(t-\tau) = 1$ for $t > \tau$.

Problem 2.5 Find the inverse transform $F(t)$ of each of the following Laplace transforms:

(a) $7e^{-2\pi s/7}/(s^2+2s+50)$ (b) $2e^{3(1-\frac{1}{2}s)}\sinh(3+\frac{1}{2}s)/(s+6)^{\frac{3}{2}}$
(c) $(e^{-as}-e^{-bs})^2/s^2$ $b > a > 0$.

Solution. (a) We have

$$F(t) = \mathcal{L}^{-1}\left\{\frac{7e^{-2\pi s/7}}{s^2+2s+50}\right\} = H\left(t-\frac{2\pi}{7}\right)G\left(t-\frac{2\pi}{7}\right)$$

where
$$G(t) = \mathscr{L}^{-1}\left\{\frac{7}{s^2+2s+50}\right\} = \mathscr{L}^{-1}\left\{\frac{7}{(s+1)^2+7^2}\right\}$$

$$= e^{-t}\mathscr{L}^{-1}\left\{\frac{7}{s^2+7^2}\right\}, \qquad \text{by Rule 3}$$

$$= e^{-t}\sin 7t.$$

Hence

$$F(t) = H\left(t-\frac{2\pi}{7}\right)e^{-(t-2\pi/7)}\sin 7\left(t-\frac{2\pi}{7}\right)$$

$$= H\left(t-\frac{2\pi}{7}\right)e^{-(t-2\pi/7)}\sin 7t$$

i.e.
$$F(t) = 0 \quad \text{for } 0 < t < 2\pi/7$$
$$= e^{-(t-2\pi/7)}\sin 7t \quad \text{for } t > 2\pi/7.$$

(b) First we write
$$2e^{3(1-\frac{1}{2}s)}\sinh(3+\tfrac{1}{2}s) = e^{3(1-\frac{1}{2}s)}(e^{3+\frac{1}{2}s} - e^{-3-\frac{1}{2}s})$$
$$= e^{6-s} - e^{-2s}$$

i.e.
$$F(t) = \mathscr{L}^{-1}\left\{\frac{e^{6-s}}{(s+6)^{\frac{5}{2}}}\right\} - \mathscr{L}^{-1}\left\{\frac{e^{-2s}}{(s+6)^{\frac{5}{2}}}\right\}$$

Now,

$$\mathscr{L}^{-1}\left\{\frac{e^6}{(s+6)^{\frac{5}{2}}}\right\} = e^{6(1-t)}\mathscr{L}^{-1}\left\{\frac{1}{s^{\frac{5}{2}}}\right\} \qquad \text{by Rule 3}$$

$$= e^{6(1-t)}\frac{t^{\frac{3}{2}}}{\frac{3}{2}\cdot\frac{1}{2}\sqrt{\pi}} = \tfrac{4}{3}e^{-6(t-1)}\frac{t^{\frac{3}{2}}}{\sqrt{\pi}}$$

Using Rule 4,

$$\mathscr{L}^{-1}\left\{\frac{e^{6-s}}{(s+6)^{\frac{5}{2}}}\right\} = \frac{4}{3\sqrt{\pi}}e^{-6(t-2)}(t-1)^{\frac{3}{2}}H(t-1)$$

$$= 0 \quad \text{for } t < 1$$

$$= \frac{4}{3\sqrt{\pi}}e^{-6(t-2)}(t-1)^{\frac{3}{2}} \quad \text{for } t > 1$$

Similarly,

$$\mathscr{L}^{-1}\left\{\frac{e^{-2s}}{(s+6)^{\frac{5}{2}}}\right\} = \frac{4}{3\sqrt{\pi}}e^{-6(t-2)}(t-2)^{\frac{3}{2}}H(t-2)$$

$$= 0 \quad \text{for } t < 2$$

$$= \frac{4}{3\sqrt{\pi}}e^{-6(t-2)}(t-2)^{\frac{3}{2}} \quad \text{for } t > 2$$

i.e. $\quad F(t) = 0 \quad \text{for } t < 1$

$$= \frac{4}{3\sqrt{\pi}}e^{-6(t-2)}(t-1)^{\frac{3}{2}} \quad \text{for } 1 < t < 2$$

$$= \frac{4}{3\sqrt{\pi}}e^{-6(t-2)}[(t-1)^{\frac{3}{2}}-(t-2)^{\frac{3}{2}}] \quad \text{for } t > 2$$

(c) We have

$$F(t) = \mathscr{L}^{-1}\left\{\frac{(e^{-as}-e^{-bs})^2}{s^2}\right\} = \mathscr{L}^{-1}\left\{\frac{e^{-2as}-2e^{-(a+b)s}+e^{-2bs}}{s^2}\right\}$$

Since $\mathscr{L}^{-1}\{1/s^2\} = t$,

$$F(t) = (t-2a)H(t-2a) - 2(t-a-b)H(t-a-b) + (t-2b)H(t-2b)$$

i.e. $\quad F(t) = 0 \quad \text{for } < t < 2a$

$$= t - 2a \quad \text{for } 2a < t < a+b$$

$$= t - 2a - 2(t-a-b) = 2b - t \quad \text{for } a+b < t < 2b$$

$$= t - 2a - 2(t-a-b) + t - 2b = 0 \quad \text{for } t > 2b$$

$F(t)$ is therefore the triangular impulse function illustrated in Fig. 2.1. $\square$

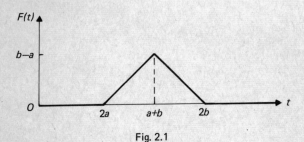

Fig. 2.1

Problem 2.6 Find $F(t) = \mathscr{L}^{-1}\{(s^{-1}-2s^{-2}+2s^{-3}-\frac{2}{3}e^{-s}s^{-3})/(1-e^{-2s})\}$

Solution. Provided $s > 0$ we can expand the denominator, in which case we find the inverse transform of

$$f(s) = \left(\frac{1}{s} - \frac{2}{s^2} + \frac{2}{s^3} - \frac{2e^{-s}}{s^3}\right)(1+e^{-2s}+e^{-4s}+e^{-6s}+\ldots)$$

34

$$= g(s) - \frac{2}{s^3}e^{-s} + g(s)e^{-2s} - \frac{2}{s^3}e^{-3s} + g(s)e^{-4s} + \ldots$$

$$\ldots + g(s)e^{-2ks} - \frac{2}{s^3}e^{-(2k+1)s} + \ldots$$

where $g(s) = s^{-1} - 2s^{-2} + 2s^{-3}$ the series being absolutely convergent when $s > 0$ so that rearrangement is permissible. We have

$$\mathcal{L}^{-1}\{s^{-1} - 2s^{-2} + 2s^{-3}\} = 1 - 2t + t^2 = (t-1)^2 = G(t)$$

$$\mathcal{L}^{-1}\{2s^{-3}\} = t^2 \qquad \mathcal{L}^{-1}\{g(s)e^{-2ks}\} = (t-1-2k)^2 H(t-2k)$$

$$\mathcal{L}^{-1}\{2s^{-3}e^{-(2k+1)s}\} = (t-1-2k)^2 H(t-2k-1)$$

Hence

$$F(t) = \mathcal{L}^{-1}\{f(s)\} = (t-1)^2 - (t-1)^2 H(t-1) + (t-3)^2 H(t-2)$$
$$- (t-3)^2 H(t-3) + \ldots + (t-2k-1)^2 H(t-2k)$$
$$- (t-2k-1)^2 H(t-2k-1) + \ldots$$

Since

$$H(t-n) = 0 \qquad \text{if } t < n$$
$$= 1 \qquad \text{if } t > n$$

we deduce that for

$$0 < t < 1, \qquad F(t) = (t-1)^2$$
$$1 < t < 2, \qquad F(t) = (t-1)^2 - (t-1)^2 = 0$$
$$\vdots \qquad \qquad \vdots$$
$$2k < t < 2k+1, \qquad F(t) = (t-2k-1)^2$$
$$2k+1 < t < 2k+2, \qquad F(t) = 0$$

where $k = 0, 1, 2, \ldots$. It follows, therefore, that $F(t)$ is a periodic function of period 2 defined by

$$F(t) = \begin{cases} (t-1)^2 & 0 < t < 1 \\ 0 & 1 < t < 2 \end{cases} \qquad \square$$

Problem 2.7 Find the inverse transform of $f(s) = 1/[s^2(k-e^{-s})], k > 0$ and deduce the inverse of $\frac{1}{2}(s+a)^{-2}e^{\frac{1}{2}s}$ cosech $\frac{1}{2}s$.

Solution. When $0 < e^{-s} < k$, i.e. $s > \ln(1/k)$,

$$f(s) = \frac{1}{s^2}\left(\frac{1}{k} + \frac{e^{-s}}{k^2} + \frac{e^{-2s}}{k^3} + \ldots + \frac{e^{-ns}}{k^{n+1}} + \ldots\right),$$

Since $\mathcal{L}^{-1}\{1/s^2\} = t$,

$$F(t) = \mathcal{L}^{-1}\{f(s)\} = \frac{t}{k} + \frac{(t-1)}{k^2}H(t-1) + \frac{(t-2)}{k^3}H(t-2) + \ldots$$

$$\ldots + \frac{(t-n)}{k^{n+1}}H(t-n) + \ldots$$

When $m < t < m+1$, where m is a positive integer,

$$H(t-n) = 1 \quad \text{for } n = 1, 2, \ldots, m$$
$$= 0 \quad n \geqslant m+1,$$

so that

$$F(t) = F_m(t) = \frac{t}{k} + \frac{t-1}{k^2} + \frac{t-2}{k^3} + \ldots + \frac{t-m}{k^{m+1}} \equiv A_m t - B_m \qquad \text{(i)}$$

where

$$A_m = \frac{1}{k} + \frac{1}{k^2} + \ldots + \frac{1}{k^{m+1}} = \frac{k^{m+1}-1}{k^{m+1}(k-1)} \qquad \text{when } k \neq 1 \qquad \text{(ii)}$$

and

$$A_m = m+1 \qquad \text{when } k = 1 \qquad \text{(iii)}$$

also,

$$B_m = \frac{1}{k^2} + \frac{2}{k^3} + \ldots + \frac{m}{k^{m+1}} = -\frac{d}{dk}\left(\frac{1}{k} + \frac{1}{k^2} + \ldots + \frac{1}{k^m}\right)$$

$$= -\frac{d}{dk}\left(\frac{k^m-1}{k^m(k-1)}\right) = \frac{mk^{-m-1} + 1 - (m+1)k^{-m}}{(k-1)^2}$$

$$\text{when } k \neq 1 \qquad \text{(iv)}$$

and

$$B_m = 1 + 2 + \ldots + m = \tfrac{1}{2}m(m+1) \qquad \text{when } k = 1 \qquad \text{(v)}$$

To deduce the second inverse transform we write

$$g(s) = \frac{e^{\frac{1}{2}s}\operatorname{cosech}\tfrac{1}{2}s}{2(s+a)^2} = \frac{1}{(s+a)^2(1-e^{-s})}$$

so that

$$g(s-a) = \frac{1}{s^2(1-e^{-s+a})} = \frac{e^{-a}}{s^2(k-e^{-s})} \qquad \text{where } k = e^{-a} > 0$$

using Rule 3,

$$\mathcal{L}^{-1}\{g(s)\} = e^{-at}\mathcal{L}^{-1}\{g(s-a)\} = e^{-a(t+1)}\mathcal{L}^{-1}\left\{\frac{1}{s^2(k-e^{-s})}\right\}$$

and, by (i)

$$\mathcal{L}^{-1}\{g(s)\} = e^{-a(t+1)}(A_m t - B_m) \quad \text{when } m < t < m+1$$

where A_m and B_m are given by (ii) and (iv) when $k = e^{-a} \neq 1$ $(a \neq 0)$ or by (iii) and (v) when $k = e^{-a} = 1$ (i.e. $a = 0$). $\qquad\square$

2.4 Inverse Laplace Transforms of s-Derivatives

Rule 5 Given $\mathcal{L}^{-1}\{f(s)\} = F(t)$ and a polynomial $M(t) = \sum_{r=1}^{n} a_r t^r$ with each a_r constant, then with $\mathcal{D} \equiv d/ds$, $\mathcal{L}^{-1}\{M(\mathcal{D})f(s)\} = M(-t)F(t)$. In particular, $\mathcal{L}^{-1}\{\mathcal{D}^n f(s)\} \equiv \mathcal{L}^{-1}\{f^{(n)}(s)\} = (-t)^n F(t)$.

Problem 2.8 Find the inverse transforms of:

(i) $1/[(s+b)^2 + a^2]^2$, (ii) $s/[(s+b)^2 + a^2]^2$

Solution. Each of the given functions can be expressed as some linear combination of $f(s)$, $g(s)$ and their derivatives, where

$$f(s) = (s+b)/[(s+b)^2 + a^2], \qquad g(s) = a/[(s+b)^2 + a^2]$$

Respective inverses of these are $F(t) = e^{-bt}\cos at$, $G(t) = e^{-bt}\sin at$. Differentiating $f(s)$, we have, writing Δ for $(s+b)^2 + a^2$,

$$f'(s) = \frac{1}{\Delta} - \frac{2(s+b)^2}{\Delta^2} = -\frac{1}{\Delta} + \frac{2a^2}{\Delta^2}, \qquad \Delta \equiv (s+b)^2 + a^2$$

Taking the inverse of both sides, and using Rule 5 on the left-hand side,

$$-t F(t) = -G(t)/a + 2a^2 \mathcal{L}^{-1}\{1/\Delta^2\}$$

Substituting for F and G,

$$\mathcal{L}^{-1}\left\{\frac{1}{\Delta^2}\right\} \equiv \mathcal{L}^{-1}\left\{\frac{1}{[(s+b)^2+a^2]^2}\right\} = \frac{e^{-bt}}{2a^3}(\sin at - at\cos at) \qquad \text{(i)}$$

Again, differentiating $g(s)$,

$$g'(s) = -2a(s+b)/\Delta^2$$

Taking the inverse of either side and equating them,

$$-t G(t) = -2a\mathcal{L}^{-1}\{s/\Delta^2\} - 2ab\mathcal{L}^{-1}\{1/\Delta^2\}$$

Using result (i) for this last inverse and putting $G(t) = e^{-bt}\sin at$,

$$\mathcal{L}^{-1}\left\{\frac{s}{\Delta^2}\right\} \equiv \mathcal{L}^{-1}\left\{\frac{s}{[(s+b)^2+a^2]^2}\right\}$$

$$= \frac{1}{2a}e^{-bt}t\sin at - \frac{b}{2a^3}e^{-bt}(\sin at - at\cos at) \qquad\square$$

Problem 2.9 Find the inverse of (i) $\tan^{-1}(a/s)$, (ii) $\ln(1 + k^2/s^2)$

Solution. (i) Writing $\tan^{-1}(a/s) = f(s) = \mathscr{L}\{F(t)\}$,

$$f'(s) = \frac{1}{1+(a/s)^2}\left(-\frac{a}{s^2}\right) = -\frac{a}{a^2+s^2}$$

Using Rule 5, $\mathscr{L}^{-1}\{f'(s)\} = -t\,F(t) = -\sin at$ so that

$$F(t) = \sin at/t \tag{i}$$

(ii) Writing $\ln(1+k^2/s^2) = g(s) = \mathscr{L}\{G(t)\}$,

$$g'(s) = -\frac{2k^2}{s(s^2+k^2)} = -\frac{2}{s}+\frac{2s}{(s^2+k^2)}$$

Therefore, $\mathscr{L}^{-1}\{g'(s)\} = -2+2\cos kt = -t\,G(t)$ by Rule 5, i.e.

$$G(t) = 2(1-\cos kt)/t = 4\sin^2\tfrac{1}{2}kt/t \qquad \square$$

2.5   Division by $(s+a)^n$
Rule 11   We have

$$\mathscr{L}^{-1}\{f(s)/(s+a)\} = e^{-at}\int_0^t e^{ax}F(x)\,dx$$

where $\mathscr{L}^{-1}\{f(s)\} = F(t)$. Applying the rule again

$$\mathscr{L}^{-1}\{f(s)(s+a)^{-2}\} = e^{-at}\int_0^t dy \int_0^y e^{ax}F(x)\,dx.$$

When n is a positive integer using the rule n times we have

$$\mathscr{L}^{-1}\{f(s)(s+a)^{-n}\} = e^{-at}\int_0^t\int_0^t\cdots\int_0^t e^{at}F(t)\,dt^n$$

there being n successive integrations in this case.

Problem 2.10   Evaluate the inverses of (i) $(s^3+as^2)^{-\frac{1}{2}}$, (ii) $\ln[1+(s^2+1)^{-\frac{1}{2}}]$.

Solution. (i) We write $(s^3+as^2)^{-\frac{1}{2}} = (s+a)^{-\frac{1}{2}}/s$
But $\mathscr{L}^{-1}\{s^{-\frac{1}{2}}\} = t^{-\frac{1}{2}}/\Gamma(\tfrac{1}{2}) = (\pi t)^{-\frac{1}{2}}$. Therefore, by Rule 3,

$$\mathscr{L}^{-1}\{(s+a)^{-\frac{1}{2}}\} = e^{-at}(\pi t)^{-\frac{1}{2}}$$

Using Rule 11,

$$\mathscr{L}^{-1}\{(s+a)^{-\frac{1}{2}}/s\} = \int_0^t e^{-ax}(\pi x)^{-\frac{1}{2}}\,dx$$

$$= 2(\pi a)^{-\frac{1}{2}}\int_0^{\sqrt{(at)}} e^{-v^2}\,dv = a^{-\frac{1}{2}}\mathrm{erf}\sqrt{(at)} \qquad \text{where } ax = v^2$$

(ii) Writing $\ln[1+(s^2+1)^{-\frac{1}{2}}] = g(s) = \mathscr{L}\{G(t)\}$, we have

$$g'(s) = -\frac{s(s^2+1)^{-\frac{3}{2}}}{1+(s^2+1)^{-\frac{1}{2}}} = -\frac{s}{(s^2+1)\{\sqrt{(s^2+1)}+1\}}$$

$$= -\frac{\sqrt{(s^2+1)}-1}{s(s^2+1)} = -\frac{1}{s\sqrt{(s^2+1)}}+\frac{1}{s}-\frac{s}{s^2+1}$$

Hence
$$\mathscr{L}^{-1}\{g'(s)\} = -\mathscr{L}^{-1}\{1/[s\sqrt{(s^2+1)}]\}+1-\cos t$$
To evaluate the inverse on the right-hand side we apply Rule 11 to the result $\mathscr{L}^{-1}\{(s^2+1)^{-\frac{1}{2}}\} = J_0(t)$; thus
$$\mathscr{L}^{-1}\{1/[s\sqrt{(s^2+1)}]\} = \int_0^t J_0(x)\, dx$$
so that by Rule 5
$$-t\, G(t) = \mathscr{L}^{-1}\{g'(s)\} = -\int_0^t J_0(x)\, dx+1-\cos t$$
or
$$G(t) = \left[\int_0^t J_0(x)\, dx-1+\cos t\right]\Big/t. \qquad \square$$

Problem 2.11 Evaluate $F_n(t) = \mathscr{L}\{1/[s^n(s^2+1)]\}$ where n is a non-negative inter.

Solution. When $n = 0$ we have $F_0(t) = \sin t$. For $n \geqslant 1$, Rule 11 gives
$$F_n(t) = \int_0^t \int_0^t \cdots \int_0^t \sin t\, dt^n$$
Successive application up to $n = 5$ gives

$$F_1(t) = \int_0^t \sin t\, dt = 1-\cos t \qquad F_2(t) = \int_0^t (1-\cos t)\, dt = t-\sin t$$

$$F_3(t) = \int_0^t F_2(t)\, dt = \tfrac{1}{2}t^2-1+\cos t$$

$$F_4(t) = \int_0^t F_3(t)\, dt = \tfrac{1}{6}t^3-t+\sin t$$

$$F_5(t) = \int_0^t F_4(t)\, dt = \tfrac{1}{24}t^4-\tfrac{1}{2}t^2+1-\cos t$$

It would appear that the general expression for $F_n(t)$ when n is even and equal to $2m$ (m is an integer) has the form

$$F_{2m}(t) = \frac{t^{2m-1}}{(2m-1)!}-\frac{t^{2m-3}}{(2m-3)!}+\cdots+(-1)^{m+1}t+(-1)^m\sin t, \qquad m \geqslant 1$$

Assuming the validity of this result up to and including $n = 2m$ (it is true for both $m = 1$ and 2), we find the formula for F_{2m+2} by using

$$F_{2m+2}(t) = \int_0^t \int_0^t F_{2m}(t)\, dt^2.\text{ But}$$

$$\int_0^t \int_0^t t^k\, dt^2 = \frac{t^{k+2}}{(k+2)(k+1)} \qquad (k > 0)$$

$$\int_0^t \int_0^t \sin t\, dt^2 = \int_0^t (1-\cos t)\, dt = t-\sin t$$

Therefore

$$F_{2m+2}(t) = \frac{t^{2m+1}}{(2m+1)(2m)(2m-1)!} - \frac{t^{2m-1}}{(2m-1)(2m-2)(2m-3)!} + \cdots$$

$$+ (-1)^{m+1}\frac{t^3}{3.2} + (-1)^m(t - \sin t)$$

$$= \frac{t^{2m+1}}{(2m+1)!} - \frac{t^{2m-1}}{(2m-1)!} + \cdots + (-1)^m t + (-1)^{m+1}\sin t$$

so that the assumed form for $F_{2m}(t)$ is also valid for $n = 2m+2$ and is true in general, therefore, for n an even integer. We can deduce the form when n is odd from the formula $F_{2m+1}(t) = \int_0^t F_{2m}(t)\, dt$ so that for $m \geqslant 0$

$$F_{2m+1}(t) = \frac{t^{2m}}{(2m)!} - \frac{t^{2m-2}}{(2m-2)!} + \cdots + (-1)^{m+1}\frac{t^2}{2!} + (-1)^m + (-1)^{m-1}\cos t \qquad \square$$

2.6 Method of Partial Fractions

This method is illustrated by the following problems.

Problem 2.12 Express in partial fractions the rational function

$$\frac{3s^3 + 3s^2 + 16s - 7}{(s-1)(2s-1)(s^2+4)}$$

and hence find its inverse transform.

Solution. We assume

$$\frac{3s^3 + 3s^2 + 16s - 7}{(s-1)(2s-1)(s^2+4)} = \frac{A}{s-1} + \frac{B}{2s-1} + \frac{Cs+D}{s^2+4} \qquad (1)$$

and evaluate the constants A, B, C and D as follows. Multiplying throughout by $(s-1)(2s-1)(s^2+4)$,

$$3s + 3s + 16s - 7 = A(2s-1)(s^2+4) + B(s-1)(s^2+4) + (Cs+D)(s-1)(2s-1)$$

Equating coefficients of powers of s,

   (i) $3 = 2A + B + 2C$ (ii) $3 = -A - B - 3C + 2D$

  (iii) $16 = 8A + 4B + C - 3D$ (iv) $-7 = -4A - 4B + D$

Eliminating $2A + B$ between (i) and (iii), $A + B$ between (iii) and (iv) gives $7C + 3D = -4$, $7D - 12C = 19$ from which it follows that $C = -1$ and $D = 1$. Substituting these values into (i) and (ii), we find that $2A + B = 5$, $A + B = 2$, from which $A = 3$, and $B = -1$, i.e. the partial fractions are

$$\frac{3}{s-1} - \frac{1}{2s-1} - \frac{s-1}{s^2+4}$$

consequently,

40

$$\mathcal{L}^{-1}\left\{\frac{3s^3+3s^2+16s-7}{(s-1)(2s-1)(s^2+4)}\right\} = 3e^t - \tfrac{1}{2}e^{\frac{1}{2}t} - \cos 2t + \tfrac{1}{2}\sin 2t$$

Alternatively, the coefficients A, B, C, D can be found as follows. In (1) multiply throughout by the factor $(s-1)$ and then let $s \to 1$. We have

$$\frac{3s^3+3s^2+16s-7}{(2s-1)(s^2+4)} = A+(s-1)\left(\frac{B}{2s-1}+\frac{Cs+D}{s^2+4}\right).$$

Therefore when $s \to 1$,

$$\frac{3+3+16-7}{5} = 3 = A.$$

Similarly, to obtain B, multiply throughout by $(2s-1)$ and let $s \to \tfrac{1}{2}$, i.e.

$$B = \frac{3(\tfrac{1}{2})^3+3(\tfrac{1}{2})^2+16(\tfrac{1}{2})-7}{(\tfrac{1}{2}-1)((\tfrac{1}{2})^2+4)} = -1.$$

C and D are now found by multiplying throughout by the factor (s^2+4) and letting $s \to \pm 2i$ or, what is equivalent, letting $s \to 2i$ and equating real and imaginary parts. Therefore,

$$2iC+D = \frac{24i^3+12i^2+32i-7}{(2i-1)(4i-1)} = \frac{8i-19}{-6i-7}$$

$$= \left(\frac{8i-19}{-6i-7}\right).\left(\frac{6i-7}{6i-7}\right) = \frac{85-170i}{85} = 1-2i$$

Hence $C = -1$ and $D = 1$, as before. $\qquad\square$

Problem 2.13 Find $\mathcal{L}^{-1}\left\{\dfrac{(2s^4+2s^3-45s^2+56s+128)}{(s+4)^2(s-2)^3}\right\}$

Solution. The partial fractions of the given function are of the form

$$\frac{2s^4+2s^3-45s^2+56s+128}{(s+4)^2(s-2)^3} = \frac{A}{(s+4)^2}+\frac{B}{s+4}+\frac{C}{(s-2)^3}+\frac{D}{(s-2)^2}+\frac{F}{s-2} \quad (1)$$

To find A, multiply throughout by $(s+4)^2$ and allow $s \to -4$, i.e.

$$A = \frac{512-128-720-224+128}{-216} = 2 \quad (2)$$

Again, multiplying both sides by $(s-2)^3$ and letting $s \to 2$ we find C.

$$C = \frac{32+16-180+112+128}{36} = 3 \quad (3)$$

This method fails to determine the three constants B, D and E because the remaining roots are repeated roots. To evaluate these unknowns multiply

(1) throughout by s and let $s \to \infty$, then

$$2 = B + E \tag{4}$$

Putting $s = 0$ and $s = 1$ consecutively in (1), and using (2) and (3), we find

$$-3 = B + D - 2E \qquad -14 = B + 5D - 5E \tag{5}$$

The solution of (4) and (5) gives $B = E = 1$, $D = -2$. Consequently,

$$\mathscr{L}^{-1}\left\{\frac{2s^4 + 2s^3 - 45s^2 + 56s + 128}{(s+4)^2(s-2)^3}\right\}$$

$$= \mathscr{L}^{-1}\left\{\frac{2}{(s+4)^2} + \frac{1}{(s+4)} + \frac{3}{(s-2)^3} - \frac{2}{(s-2)^2} + \frac{1}{s-2}\right\}$$

$$= (2t+1)e^{-4t} + (\tfrac{1}{2}t^2 - 2t + 1)e^{2t} \qquad \qquad \square$$

2.7 Convolution Rule

Rule 12 Defining the *convolution* $F_1 * F_2$ of two given functions $F_1 = F_1(t)$, $F_2 = F_2(t)$ as $F_1 * F_2 = \int_0^t F_1(x)F_2(t-x)\,dx$, we have

$$\mathscr{L}\{F_1 * F_2\} = f_1(s)f_2(s) \qquad \text{where } \mathscr{L}\{F_1(t)\} = f_1(s)$$

and

$$\mathscr{L}\{F_2(t)\} = f_2(s).$$

Interchanging f_1 and f_2, or substituting $u = t - x$ in the integral gives $F_1 * F_2 = F_2 * F_1$.

Problem 2.14 Combining Rules 11 and 12 prove that the *n*-fold repeated integral

$$\int_0^t \int_0^t \cdots \int_0^t F(t)\,dt^n = \int_0^t F(x)(t-x)^{n-1}\,dx/(n-1)!$$

Solution. The repeated integral represents the inverse $\mathscr{L}^{-1}\{f(s)s^{-n}\}$. But $\mathscr{L}^{-1}\{f(s)\} = F(t)$ and $\mathscr{L}^{-1}\{s^{-n}\} = t^{n-1}/(n-1)!$ so that by Rule 12,

$$\mathscr{L}^{-1}\{f(s)s^{-n}\} = \int_0^t F(x)\frac{(t-x)^{n-1}}{(n-1)!}\,dx \qquad \qquad \square$$

Problem 2.15 Evaluate the following using Rule 12:

(a) $\mathscr{L}^{-1}\left\{\dfrac{1}{(s+\alpha)^2(s-\beta)}\right\}$, (b) $\mathscr{L}^{-1}\{s/(s^2+a^2)^2\}$, (c) $\mathscr{L}^{-1}\{s/(s^2+a^2)^3\}$

Solution. (a) Choosing $f_1(s) = 1/(s+\alpha)^2$ and $f_2(s) = 1/(s-\beta)$,

$$F_1(t) = \mathscr{L}^{-1}\{f_1(s)\} = te^{-\alpha t}, \qquad F_2(t) = \mathscr{L}^{-1}\{f_2(s)\} = e^{\beta t},$$

Hence

$$\mathcal{L}^{-1}\{f_1(s)f_2(s)\} = F_1 * F_2 = \int_0^t u e^{-\alpha u} e^{\beta(t-u)}\, du = e^{\beta t}\int_0^t e^{-(\alpha+\beta)u}\, u\, du$$

$$= e^{\beta t}\left[-\frac{u e^{-(\alpha+\beta u)}}{\alpha+\beta} - \frac{e^{-(\alpha+\beta)u}}{(\alpha+\beta)^2}\right]_0^t$$

$$= \frac{e^{\beta t}}{(\alpha+\beta)^2} - \frac{e^{-\alpha t}}{(\alpha+\beta)}\left(t + \frac{1}{\alpha+\beta}\right)$$

(b) Since $s^2/(s^2+a^2)^2 = [s/(s^2+a^2)]^2$, we choose $f_1(s) = f_2(s) = s/(s^2+a^2)$ so that $F_1(t) = F_2(t) = \cos at$ and

$$\mathcal{L}^{-1}\{s^2/(s^2+a^2)^2\} = F_1 * F_2 = \int_0^t \cos a \cos a(t-x)\, dx$$

$$= \tfrac{1}{2}\int_0^t [\cos at + \cos a(2x-t)]\, dx$$

$$= \tfrac{1}{2}\cos at\, [x]_0^t + \frac{1}{4a}[\sin a(2x-t)]_0^t$$

$$= (at\cos at + \sin at)/(2a)$$

(c) Here, we choose $f_2(s) = s/(s^2+a^2)$ so that $F_2(t) = \cos at$ and $f_1(s) = (s^2+a^2)^{-2}$. To find $F_1(t)$ we can use the previous result (b) for, since

$$\frac{a^2}{(s^2+a^2)^2} = \frac{1}{(s^2+a^2)} - \frac{s^2}{(s^2+a^2)^2}$$

then taking inverses,

$$a^2 F_1(t) = \mathcal{L}^{-1}\left\{\frac{a^2}{(s^2+a^2)^2}\right\} = \frac{1}{a}\sin at - \left(\tfrac{1}{2}t\cos at + \frac{1}{2a}\sin at\right)$$

i.e. $$F_1(t) = (\sin at - at\cos at)/2a^3.$$

Using Rule 12, we have

$$\mathcal{L}^{-1}\left\{\frac{s}{(s^2+a^2)^3}\right\} = F_1 * F_2 = \frac{1}{2a^3}\int_0^t (\sin ax - ax\cos ax)\cos a(x-t)\, dx$$

$$= \frac{1}{4a^3}\int_0^t [\sin a(2x-t) + \sin at - ax\cos a(2x-t)$$

$$- ax\cos at]\, dx$$

We consider separately the four elements of this integral.

$$\int_0^t \sin a(2x-t)\, dx = \frac{1}{2a}[-\cos a(2x-t)]_0^t = 0$$

43

$$\int_0^t \sin at \, dx = \sin at \int_0^t dx = t \sin at$$

$$\int_0^t ax \cos a(2x-t) \, dx = \left[2ax \sin a(2x-t) + \frac{1}{4a} \cos a(2x-t) \right]_0^t 4a$$

$$= \tfrac{1}{2} t \sin at$$

$$\int_0^t ax \cos at \, dx = a \cos at \int_0^t x \, dx = \tfrac{1}{2} at^2 \cos at$$

Hence

$$\mathscr{L}^{-1}\{s(s^2+a^2)^{-3}\} = (t \sin at - \tfrac{1}{2} t \sin at - \tfrac{1}{2} at^2 \cos at)/4a^2$$

$$= t(\sin at - at \cos at)/8a^3.$$

It should be noticed that if the roles of f_1 and f_2 were interchanged, the corresponding integrals would be a little more difficult to manipulate, but the final result would be the same. $\qquad\square$

2.8 Heaviside Formula Given that $M(s)$ and $N(s)$ are polynomials of degree m and n respectively with $m < n$ and that $N(s)$ has n *distinct* zeros α_k, $k = 1, 2, 3, \ldots, n$, none of which is a zero of $M(s)$, then

$$\mathscr{L}^{-1}\left\{\frac{M(s)}{N(s)}\right\} = \sum_{k=1}^n \frac{M(\alpha_k)}{N'(\alpha_k)} e^{\alpha_k t}$$

If, instead, $N(s) = 0$ has a repeated root (say α_1) of multiplicity r while the remaining roots $\alpha_2, \alpha_3, \ldots, \alpha_n$ are not repeated, the corresponding result is

$$\mathscr{L}^{-1}\left\{\frac{M(s)}{N(s)}\right\} = \sum_{k=2}^n \frac{M(\alpha_k)}{N'(\alpha_k)} e^{\alpha_k t} + \left[\frac{A_1 t^{r-1}}{(r-1)!} + \frac{A_2 t^{r-2}}{(r-2)!} + \ldots + A_r \right] e^{\alpha_1 t}$$

where

$$A_p = \lim_{s \to \alpha_1} \frac{1}{(p-1)!} \frac{d^p}{ds^p} \left[(s-\alpha_1)^r \frac{M(s)}{N(s)} \right], \qquad p = 1, 2, \ldots, r$$

To prove the first result we write

$$\frac{M(s)}{N(s)} = \frac{c_1}{s-\alpha_1} + \frac{c_2}{s-\alpha_2} + \ldots + \frac{c_k}{s-\alpha_k} + \ldots + \frac{c_n}{s-\alpha_n}$$

where c_k are constants to be determined. To evaluate c_k we multiply both sides by $s - \alpha_k$ and allow $s \to \alpha_k$; the limit is obtained by appeal to l'Hôpital's rule,

$$c_k = \lim_{s \to \alpha_k} \frac{M(s)(s-\alpha_k)}{N(s)} = M(\alpha_k) \lim_{s \to \alpha_k} \frac{(s-\alpha_k)}{N(s)}$$

$$= M(\alpha_k) \lim_{s \to \alpha_k} \frac{d(s-\alpha_k)/ds}{dN(s)/ds} = \frac{M(\alpha_k)}{N'(\alpha_k)}$$

The result follows from

$$\mathscr{L}^{-1}\left\{\frac{M(s)}{N(s)}\right\} = \sum_{k=1}^{n} \mathscr{L}^{-1}\left\{\frac{c_k}{s-\alpha_k}\right\} = \sum_{k=1}^{n} c_k e^{\alpha_k t}$$

Problem 2.16 Evaluate $\mathscr{L}^{-1}\{s/(s^4+4a^4)\}$

Solution. Here, $M(s) = s$, $N(s) = s^4+4a^4 \equiv (s^2+2ia^2)(s^2-2ia^2)$, the latter having distinct zeros given by $\alpha_1 = (1+i)a$, $\alpha_2 = (1-i)a$, $\alpha_3 = (-1+i)a$, $\alpha_4 = (-1-i)a$. Hence

$$c_1 = \frac{M(\alpha_1)}{N'(\alpha_1)} = \frac{\alpha_1}{4\alpha_1^3} = \frac{\alpha_1^2}{-16a^4} = -\frac{i}{8a^2},$$

since $\alpha_1^4+4a^4 = 0$. Similarly, $c_2 = -\alpha_2^2/16a^4 = i/8a^2$, $c_3 = i/8a^2$, $c_4 = -i/8a^2$. Therefore

$$\mathscr{L}^{-1}\left\{\frac{s}{(s^4+4a^4)}\right\} = \frac{i}{8a^2}(-e^{(1+i)at}+e^{(1-i)at}+e^{(-1+i)at}-e^{(-1-i)at})$$

$$= \frac{i}{8a^2}(-2ie^{at}\sin at + 2ie^{-at}\sin at) \to \frac{\sin at}{4a^2}(e^{at}-e^{-at})$$

$$= \frac{1}{2a^2}\sin at \sinh at \qquad\qquad \square$$

Problem 2.17 Find $\mathscr{L}^{-1}\{(2s^3+3s^2+10s-3)/[(s^2-2s+5)(s^2+4s+13)]\}$

Solution. Since

$$s^2-2s+5 = (s-1)^2+4 \equiv (s-\alpha_1)(s-\alpha_2),$$
$$s^2+4s+13 = (s+2)^2+9 \equiv (s-\alpha_3)(s-\alpha_4)$$

where $\alpha_1 = 1-2i$, $\alpha_2 = 1+2i$, $\alpha_3 = -2-3i$, $\alpha_4 = -2+3i$, we can use the Heaviside formula taking

$$c_k = \frac{M(\alpha_k)}{N'(\alpha_k)} = \frac{2\alpha_k^3+3\alpha_k^2+10\alpha_k-3}{2(\alpha_k-1)(\alpha_k^2+4\alpha_k+13)+2(\alpha_k^2-2\alpha_k+5)(\alpha_k+2)}$$

$$k = 1,2,3,4$$

Now

$$M(\alpha_1) = 2(1-2i)^3+3(1-2i)^2+10(1-2i)-3$$
$$= 2(-11+2i)+3(-3-4i)+10(1-2i)-3 = -24-28i,$$

and since $\alpha_1^2-2\alpha_1+5 = 0$

$$N'(\alpha_1) = 2(1-2i-1)[(1-2i)^2+4(1-2i)+13] = -4i(14-12i)$$

45

Hence $c_1 = \dfrac{M(\alpha_1)}{N'(\alpha_1)} = \dfrac{(-24-28i)}{(-56i-48)} = \tfrac{1}{2}$

Since $\alpha_2 = \bar{\alpha}_1$ (complex conjugate of α_1) we have

$$c_2 = \frac{M(\alpha_2)}{N'(\alpha_2)} = \frac{M(\bar{\alpha}_1)}{N'(\bar{\alpha}_1)} = \bar{c}_1 = \tfrac{1}{2}$$

Again
$$M(\alpha_3) = 2(-2-3i)^3 + 3(-2-3i)^2 + 10(-2-3^i) - 3$$
$$= 2(46-9i) + 3(-5+12i) + 10(-2-3i) - 3 = 54 - 12i$$

and
$$N'(\alpha_3) = 2[(-2-3i)^2 - 2(-2-3i)+5](-3i) = -6i(4+18i)$$
Since $\alpha_3^2 + 4\alpha_3 + 13 = 0$. Hence
$$c_3 = \frac{M(\alpha_3)}{N'(\alpha_3)} = \frac{(54-12i)}{-6i(4+18i)} = \tfrac{1}{2}$$

and since $\alpha_4 = \bar{\alpha}_3$, $c_4 = \bar{c}_3 = \tfrac{1}{2}$ also. Finally
$$\mathscr{L}^{-1}\left\{\frac{M(s)}{N(s)}\right\} = \tfrac{1}{2}(e^{(1-2i)t} + e^{(1+2i)t} + e^{(-2-3i)t} + e^{(-2+3i)t}$$
$$= e^t\cos 2t + e^{-2t}\cos 3t$$

Alternative solution. We can write
$$\frac{2s^3 + 3s^2 + 10s - 3}{(s^2 - 2s + 5)(s^2 + 4s + 13)} = \frac{As+B}{s^2 - 2s + 5} + \frac{Cs+D}{s^2 + 4s + 13}$$

To determine the constants, we could equate coefficients of powers of s after multiplying throughout by the denominator of the left-hand side, or proceed as follows. Putting $s = 0$; we have $13B + 5D = -3$, whereas $s = 1$, $s = -1$ respectively give

$$9(A+B) + 2(C+D) = 6, \qquad 5(B-A) + 4(D-C) = -6$$

Multiplying throughout by s and allowing $s \to \infty$ gives $2 = A + C$. Solving, we find $A = C = 1$, $B = -1$, $D = 2$. Hence, by Rule 3,

$$\mathscr{L}^{-1}\left\{\frac{2s^3 + 3s^2 + 10s - 3}{(s^2 - 2s + 5)(s^2 + 4s + 13)}\right\} = \mathscr{L}^{-1}\left\{\frac{s-1}{s^2 - 2s + 5}\right\} + \mathscr{L}^{-1}\left\{\frac{s+2}{s^2 + 4s + 13}\right\}$$
$$= \mathscr{L}^{-1}\left\{\frac{s-1}{(s-1)^2 + 4}\right\} + \mathscr{L}^{-1}\left\{\frac{s+2}{(s+2)^2 + 9}\right\}$$
$$= e^t\cos 2t + e^{-2t}\cos 3t \qquad \square$$

Problem 2.18 Find the inverse transform of $\sinh[s(l-x)/c]/\sinh(sl/c)$.

Solution. Here we write $M(s) = \sinh s(l-x)/c$, $N(s) = \sinh(sl/c)$. The zeros of $N(s)$ are $s = \alpha_k = \pm ikc\pi/l$, $k = 0, 1, 2, \ldots$ and are all distinct. By the Heaviside formula, the inverse $F(t)$ is

$$F(t) = \mathscr{L}^{-1}\left\{\frac{M(s)}{N(s)}\right\} = \sum_{\alpha_k} \frac{M(\alpha_k)}{N'(\alpha_k)} e^{\alpha_k t}$$

$$= \frac{M(0)}{N'(0)} + \sum_{k=1}^{\infty} \left[\frac{M(ikc\pi/l)}{N'(ikc\pi/l)} e^{ikc\pi t/l} + \frac{M(-ikc\pi/l)}{N'(-ikc\pi/l)} e^{-ikc\pi t/l}\right]$$

$$M(ikc\pi/l) = \sinh[ik\pi(1-x/l)] = i\sin[k\pi - k\pi x/l] = i(-1)^{k+1}\sin(k\pi x/l)$$
$$N'(ikc\pi/l) = (l/c)\cosh(ik\pi) = (l/c)\cos k\pi = (-1)^k l/c$$

Replacing k by $-k$ gives two further formulae. The expression in the square brackets under summation is therefore

$$\frac{c}{l}\sin\frac{k\pi x}{l}(-ie^{ik\pi ct/l} + ie^{-ik\pi ct/l}) = \frac{2c}{l}\sin\frac{k\pi x}{l}\sin\frac{k\pi ct}{l}$$

and since $M(0) = 0$, we get

$$F(t) = \mathscr{L}^{-1}\left\{\frac{\sinh s(l-x)/c}{\sinh sl/c}\right\} = \frac{2c}{l}\sum_{k=1}^{\infty} \sin\frac{k\pi x}{l}\sin\frac{k\pi ct}{l}. \qquad \square$$

EXERCISES

Evaluate the inverse Laplace transforms of:

1. $s(1+as)^{-3}$, $s^2(1+as)^{-3}$

2. $[s(as+1)\ldots(as+n)]^{-1}$

3. $\sqrt{[(s^2+a^2)^{\frac{1}{2}}-s]}$, $s^2(s^2+a^2)^{-\frac{3}{2}}$

4. $s^{-\frac{3}{2}}e^{1/s}$

5. $s^{-\frac{1}{2}}\sin(a/s)$, $s^{-\frac{1}{2}}\cos(a/s)$

6. $(3s^3 - 7s^2 + 13s + 37)/[(s^2 - 4s + 13)(s^2 - 2s + 5)]$

7. $(s-1)^{-2}(s+2)^{-3}(5s^4 + 15s^3 + 10s^2 - 4s + 1)$

8. $(4 - e^{-as})/[s(4 + 2e^{-as})]$

Chapter 3

Elementary Applications

3.1 Evaluation of Integrals Here we state four methods by means of which Laplace transforms can be applied to evaluate certain types of integrals. We assume that $\mathscr{L}\{F(t)\} = f(s)$ and $\mathscr{L}\{G(t)\} = g(s)$.

Method 1 To evaluate an integral of the form $\int_0^t F(t-x)G(x)\,dx$ we use the Convolution Rule 12,

$$\int_0^t F(t-x)G(x)\,dx = \mathscr{L}^{-1}\{f(s)g(s)\}$$

Method 2 To evaluate $\int_0^\infty F(t)\,dt$, provided that we can invert the order of taking the limit with integration, we have

$$\int_0^\infty F(t)\,dt = \lim_{s \to 0+} \int_0^\infty e^{-st}F(t)\,dt = \lim_{s \to 0+} f(s)$$

Method 3 Formally we have $\int_0^\infty f(x)G(x)\,dx = \int_0^\infty F(x)g(x)\,dx$ for,

$$\int_0^\infty f(x)G(x)\,dx = \int_0^\infty G(x)\left(\int_0^\infty e^{-xt}F(t)\,dt\right)dx$$

$$= \int_0^\infty F(t)\left(\int_0^\infty e^{-xt}G(x)\,dt\right)dt = \int_0^\infty F(t)g(t)\,dt$$

when the change of order of integration is valid.

Method 4 To evaluate $F(t) = \int_0^\infty G(xt)k(x)\,dx$ provided that taking the Laplace transform within the integral is justifiable we have

$$\mathscr{L}\{F(t)\} = f(s) = \int_0^\infty k(x)\,dx \int_0^\infty e^{-st}G(xt)\,dt = \int_0^\infty k(x)g(s/x)x^{-1}\,dx$$

i.e.
$$F(t) = \mathscr{L}^{-1}\left\{\int_0^\infty g(s/x)k(x)x^{-1}\,dx\right\}$$

Problem 3.1 For the Beta function $B(m,n)$ defined by

$$B(m,n) = \int_0^1 x^{m-1}(1-x)^{n-1}\,dx, \qquad m > 0, n > 0$$

prove that $B(m,n) = \Gamma(m)\Gamma(n)/\Gamma(m+n)$.

Deduce that $\int_0^{\frac{1}{2}\pi} \sin^6\theta \cos^8\theta\,d\theta = 5\pi/2^{12}$.

Solution. Here we use Method 1. Writing $M(t) = \int_0^t x^{m-1}(t-x)^{n-1}\,dx$ and using the convolution rule we have

48

$$\mathcal{L}\{M(t)\} = \mathcal{L}\{t^{m-1}\}\mathcal{L}\{t^{n-1}\} = \frac{\Gamma(m)}{s^m} \cdot \frac{\Gamma(n)}{s^n} = \frac{\Gamma(m)\Gamma(n)}{s^{m+n}}, \quad m > 0, n > 0$$

using section 1.9. Taking the inverse transform,

$$M(t) = \frac{\Gamma(m)\Gamma(n)}{\Gamma(m+n)} t^{m+n-1} = \int_0^t x^{m-1}(t-x)^{n-1} \, dx$$

Hence $M(1) = B(m, n) = \Gamma(m)\Gamma(n)/\Gamma(m+n)$.

If we put $x = \sin^2\theta$ in the integral which defines $B(m, n)$,

$$B(m, n) = \int_0^{\frac{1}{2}\pi} \sin^{2m-2}\theta \cos^{2n-2}\theta \, 2\sin\theta\cos\theta \, d\theta$$

$$= 2\int_0^{\frac{1}{2}\pi} \sin^{2m-1}\theta \cos^{2n-1}\theta \, d\theta$$

i.e. $\int_0^{\frac{1}{2}\pi} \sin^{2m-1}\theta \cos^{2n-1}\theta \, d\theta = \frac{1}{2}\Gamma(m)\Gamma(n)/\Gamma(m+n)$

If we now choose $m = \frac{7}{2}$, $n = \frac{9}{2}$ we have
$\int_0^{\frac{1}{2}\pi} \sin^6\theta \cos^8\theta \, d\theta = \frac{1}{2}\Gamma(\frac{7}{2})\Gamma(\frac{9}{2})/\Gamma(8)$

$$= \frac{(\frac{5}{2})(\frac{3}{2})(\frac{1}{2})\sqrt{\pi} \cdot (\frac{7}{2})(\frac{5}{2})(\frac{3}{2})(\frac{1}{2})\sqrt{\pi}}{2 \cdot 7 \cdot 6 \cdot 5 \cdot 4 \cdot 3 \cdot 2 \cdot 1} = \frac{5\pi}{2^{12}} \qquad \square$$

Problem 3.2 Evaluate $F(t) = \int_0^t J_0(t-u)\phi(u) \, du$ when $\phi(u)$ is equal to
(i) $J_0(u)$, (ii) $\sin u$, (iii) $J_1(u)/u$.

Solution. We use the convolution rule 12, i.e. Method 1
$$\mathcal{L}\{F(t)\} = \mathcal{L}\{J_0(t)\}\mathcal{L}\{\phi(t)\} = (s^2+1)^{-\frac{1}{2}}\mathcal{L}\{\phi(t)\}$$

(i) $\phi(t) = J_0(t)$, $\mathcal{L}\{\phi(t)\} = (s^2+1)^{-\frac{1}{2}}$, i.e. $\mathcal{L}\{F(t)\} = 1/(s^2+1)$ or
$$F(t) = \sin t = \int_0^t J_0(t-u)J_0(u) \, du$$

(ii) $\phi(t) = \sin t$, $\mathcal{L}\{\phi(t)\} = 1/(s^2+1)$, i.e. $\mathcal{L}\{F(t)\} = (s^2+1)^{-\frac{3}{2}}$
To invert this relation, we use Problem 1.20 where
$\mathcal{L}\{J_1(t)\} = 1 - s(s^2+1)^{-\frac{1}{2}}$ and by Rule 5, we have

$$\mathcal{L}\{tJ_1(t)\} = -\frac{d}{ds}\left\{1 - \frac{s}{\sqrt{(s^2+1)}}\right\} = \frac{1}{(s^2+1)^{\frac{3}{2}}}$$

or $$F(t) = tJ_1(t) = \int_0^t J_0(t-u)\sin u \, du$$

(iii) $\phi(t) = J_1(t)/t$, and
$$\mathcal{L}\{\phi(t)\} = \int_s^\infty [1 - u(u^2+1)^{-\frac{1}{2}}] \, du \quad \text{(Rule 6)}$$

$$= [u - \sqrt{(u^2+1)}]_s^\infty = \sqrt{(s^2+1)} - s$$

since $\lim_{u \to \infty} (u - \sqrt{(u^2+1)}) = \lim_{u \to \infty} [-1/(u + \sqrt{(u^2+1)})] = 0$. Hence
$\mathscr{L}\{F(t)\} = 1 - s(s^2+1)^{-\frac{1}{2}}$ so that

$$F(t) = J_1(t) = \int_0^t J_0(t-u)J_1(u) \, du/u \qquad \square$$

Problem 3.3 Prove that $\int_0^\infty J_0(at)\cos bt \, dt = (a^2-b^2)^{-\frac{1}{2}}$ when $0 < b < a$ and has the value zero when $b > a$.

Solution. We use a modified version of Method 2. Quoting the result of Problem 1.10,

$$\mathscr{L}\{J_0(at)\} = \int_0^\infty e^{-st} J_0(at) \, dt = 1/\sqrt{(s^2+a^2)}, \qquad a > 0, s > 0$$

If now we write $s = c + ib$ where c and b are real (so that s is complex),

$$e^{-st} = e^{-ct}(\cos bt - i \sin bt),$$

and therefore

$$\int_0^\infty e^{-ct}(\cos bt - i \sin bt)J_0(at) \, dt = [(c+ib)^2 + a^2]^{-\frac{1}{2}} \qquad (c > 0)$$

$$= [c^2 + a^2 - b^2 + 2ibc]^{-\frac{1}{2}}$$

Let $c \to 0$. Then

$$\int_0^\infty J_0(at)(\cos bt - i \sin bt) \, dt = (a^2-b^2)^{-\frac{1}{2}}$$

Taking real parts of either side and noting that the right hand side is real if $b < a$ and purely imaginary if $b > a$, the result follows. $\square$

Problem 3.4 Evaluate $\int_0^\infty [\sin ax/x] \, dx$, using Method 3.

Solution. Put $G(x) = \sin ax$ so that $g(s) = a/(s^2+a^2)$; and put $f(s) = 1/s$, so that $F(t) = 1$. Then

$$\int_0^\infty G(x)f(x) \, dx = \int_0^\infty \frac{\sin ax}{x} \, dx = \int_0^\infty F(x)g(x) \, dx$$

$$= \int_0^\infty \frac{a \, dx}{x^2+a^2} = \left[\tan^{-1}\left(\frac{x}{a}\right)\right]_0^\infty = \frac{1}{2}\pi \qquad \square$$

Problem 3.5 Show that $\int_0^\infty [\cos tx/(x^2+1)] \, dx = \frac{1}{2}\pi e^{-t}$.

Solution. Here we use Method 4.

$$\mathscr{L}\left\{\int_0^\infty \frac{\cos tx}{x^2+1} \, dx\right\} = \int_0^\infty \mathscr{L}\{\cos tx\} \frac{dx}{x^2+1} = \int_0^\infty \frac{s}{s^2+x^2} \cdot \frac{dx}{x^2+1}$$

$$= \int_0^\infty \left(\frac{1}{x^2+1} - \frac{1}{x^2+s^2}\right) \frac{s \, dx}{s^2-1}$$

$$= \frac{s}{s^2-1}\left[\tan^{-1}x - \frac{1}{s}\tan^{-1}\frac{x}{s}\right]_0^\infty$$

$$= \frac{s}{s^2-1}\left(1 - \frac{1}{s}\right)\frac{\pi}{2} = \frac{\pi}{2(s+1)}$$

Taking the inverse transform produces the result

$$\int_0^\infty [\cos tx/(x^2+1)]\,dx = \tfrac{1}{2}\pi e^{-t} \qquad \square$$

Problem 3.6 Given that $\Gamma(a)\Gamma(1-a) = \pi\,\mathrm{cosec}\,a\pi$ when $0 < a < 1$, prove that

$$F(t) = \int_0^\infty \sin tx^p\,dx = \frac{\pi\sec(\tfrac{1}{2}\pi/p)}{2pt^{1/p}\Gamma(1-1/p)} \qquad \text{when } p > 1.$$

Evaluate when $p = 2$.

Solution. Using Method 4, we have

$$f(s) = \mathcal{L}\{F(t)\} = \int_0^\infty \mathcal{L}\{\sin tx^p\}dx = \int_0^\infty \frac{x^p}{s^2+x^{2p}}\,dx$$

which we can convert into a Beta function by the substitution $x^p = s\tan\theta$, i.e.

$$f(s) = \frac{1}{ps^{1-1/p}}\int_0^{\tfrac{1}{2}\pi} (\tan\theta)^{1/p}\,d\theta = \frac{1}{ps^{1-1/p}}\int_0^{\tfrac{1}{2}\pi} \sin\theta)^{1/p}(\cos\theta)^{-1/p}\,d\theta$$

Using Problem 3.1, $B(m,n) = 2\int_0^{\tfrac{1}{2}\pi} \sin^{2m-1}\theta\cos^{2n-1}\theta\,d\theta$, and therefore

$$f(s) = B\left(\frac{1}{2}+\frac{1}{2p},\frac{1}{2}-\frac{1}{2p}\right)\Big/(2ps^{1-1/p})$$

In the same Problem we proved that $B(m,n) = \Gamma(m)\Gamma(n)/\Gamma(m+n)$. Hence, using $\Gamma(1) = 1$ and the given formula with $a = \tfrac{1}{2}+\tfrac{1}{2}p < 1$ (since $p > 1$),

$$B\left(\frac{1}{2}+\frac{1}{2p},\frac{1}{2}-\frac{1}{2p}\right) = \Gamma\left(\frac{1}{2}+\frac{1}{2p}\right)\Gamma\left(\frac{1}{2}-\frac{1}{2p}\right) = \pi\,\mathrm{cosec}\left(\frac{1}{2}+\frac{1}{2p}\right)\pi = \pi\sec\frac{\pi}{2p}$$

Inverting, using the result in Section 1.9,

$$F(t) = \mathcal{L}^{-1}\{f(s)\} = \mathcal{L}^{-1}\left\{\frac{\pi\sec(\tfrac{1}{2}\pi/p)}{2ps^{1-1/p}}\right\} = \frac{\pi\sec(\tfrac{1}{2}\pi/p)}{2pt^{1/p}\Gamma(1-1/p)}$$

When $p = 2$,

$$F(t) = \frac{\pi\sec\tfrac{1}{4}\pi}{4t^{\frac{1}{2}}\Gamma(\tfrac{1}{2})} = \left(\frac{\pi}{8t}\right)^{\frac{1}{2}}. \qquad \square$$

3.2 Solution of Ordinary Differential Equations with Constant Coefficients

The method applies the use of Rule 8 to the Laplace transform of the whole equation. Since this rule depends on the initial conditions of the differentiated function, these conditions are automatically contained in the final solution of the given differential equation when the inverse is found. The method is illustrated in the following problems.

Problem 3.7 Solve $X'' + n^2 X = a \sin pt$ where $X(0) = 1$, $X'(0) = -3$, n, p and a being positive real constants.

Solution. Let $\mathscr{L}\{X(t)\} = x(s)$, then using Rule 8,

$$\mathscr{L}\{X'(t)\} = sx - X(0) = sx - 1 \qquad \text{since } X(0) = 1$$
$$\mathscr{L}\{X''(t)\} = s^2 x - s X(0) - X'(0) = s^2 x - s + 3 \qquad \text{since } X(0) = 1,$$
$$X'(0) = -3$$

Taking Laplace transforms of both sides of the differential equation and using the above we have

$$s^2 x - s + 3 + n^2 x = a \mathscr{L}\{\sin pt\} = ap/(s^2 + p^2)$$

i.e.
$$x = \frac{s-3}{s^2 + n^2} + \frac{pa}{(s^2 + n^2)(s^2 + p^2)}$$

If $p \neq n$, we can split the last term into partial fractions

$$x = \frac{s}{s^2 + n^2} - \frac{3}{s^2 + n^2} + \frac{pa}{p^2 - n^2}\left(\frac{1}{s^2 + n^2} - \frac{1}{s^2 + p^2}\right)$$

of which the inverse is

$$X = \cos nt - \frac{3}{n}\sin nt + \frac{pa}{p^2 - n^2}\left(\frac{1}{n}\sin nt - \frac{1}{p}\sin pt\right), \quad p \neq n$$

If $p = n$,

$$x = \frac{(s-3)}{(s^2 + n^2)} + \frac{na}{(s^2 + n^2)^2}$$

Using the convolution rule

$$\mathscr{L}^{-1}\{n^2/(s^2 + n^2)^2\} = \int_0^t \sin nu \sin n(t-u)\, du$$

$$= \frac{1}{2}\int_0^t [\cos n(2u-t) - \cos nt]\, du$$

$$= \frac{1}{2}\left[\frac{1}{2n}\sin n(2u-t) - u \cos nt\right]_0^t = \frac{1}{2n}(\sin nt - nt \cos nt)$$

so that when $p = n$, the inverse is

$$X = \cos nt - \frac{3}{n}\sin nt + \frac{a}{2n^2}(\sin nt - nt \cos nt) \qquad \square$$

Problem 3.8 Solve $X''' - 6X'' + 12X' - 8X = t^3 e^{2t}$, where $X(0) = 1$, $X'(0) = -1$, $X''(0) = -2$.

Solution. Using Rule 8 with the given initial values, we have $\mathscr{L}\{X\} = x$, $\mathscr{L}\{X'\} = sx - 1$, $\mathscr{L}\{X''\} = s^2 x - s + 1$, $\mathscr{L}\{X'''\} = s^3 x - s^2 + s + 2$. Equating Laplace transforms of the two sides of the equation,

$$s^3 x - s^2 + s + 2 - 6(s^2 x - s + 1) + 12(sx - 1) - 8x = \mathscr{L}\{t^3 e^{2t}\} = 6/(s-2)^4$$

i.e.
$$(s^3 - 6s^2 + 12s - 8)x - s^2 + 7s - 16 = 6/(s-2)^4$$

But
$$s^3 - 6s^2 + 12s - 8 \equiv (s-2)^3,$$

and so
$$x = (s^2 - 7s + 16)(s-2)^{-3} + 6(s-2)^{-7}$$

Again, $s^2 - 7s + 16 = (s-2)^2 - 3(s-2) + 6$, so that

$$x = (s-2)^{-1} - 3(s-2)^{-2} + 6(s-2)^{-3} + 6(s-2)^{-7}$$

Using $\mathscr{L}^{-1}\{n!/(s-2)^{n+1}\} = t^n e^{2t}$, $n \geqslant 0$, we have the inverse

$$X = \mathscr{L}^{-1}\{x\} = e^{2t}\left(1 - 3t + 3t^2 + \frac{t^6}{120}\right) \qquad \square$$

Problem 3.9 Solve $X'' - 2X' + 5X = e^{-2t}(4\cos 3t + 18\sin 3t)$ given that $X(0) = 2$, $X'(0) = -1$.

Solution. Here, $\mathscr{L}\{X'\} = sx - 2$, $\mathscr{L}\{X''\} = s^2 x - 2s + 1$ so that

$$s^2 x - 2s + 1 - 2(sx - 2) + 5x = 4\mathscr{L}\{e^{-2t}\cos 3t\} + 18\mathscr{L}\{e^{-2t}\sin 3t\}$$

Consequently

$$(s^2 - 2s + 5)x - 2s + 5 = \frac{4(s+2)}{(s+2)^2 + 3^2} + \frac{54}{(s+2)^2 + 3^2}$$

which rearranges to give

$$x = \frac{(2s^3 + 3s^2 + 10s - 3)}{(s^2 - 2s + 5)(s^2 + 4s + 13)}$$

The inverse of this function has already been found in the solution to Problem 2.17. The result is

$$X = e^t \cos 2t + e^{-2t}\cos 3t \qquad \square$$

Problem 3.10 Solve $X^{(4)} + 3X'' + 2X = e^{-t}H(t-2)$ where H denotes the Heaviside step function given that $X(0) = X'(0) = X'''(0) = 0$, $X''(0) = 1$.

Solution. Let $\mathscr{L}\{X(t)\} = x(s)$. Then

$$\mathscr{L}\{X^{(4)}\} = s^4 x - s^3 X(0) - s^2 X'(0) - s X''(0) - X'''(0) = s^4 x - s$$
$$\mathscr{L}\{X''\} = s^2 x - s X(0) - X'(0) = s^2 x$$

Also, since $\mathscr{L}\{H(t-a)\} = e^{-as}s$, $a > 0$, we have
$\mathscr{L}\{e^{-t}H(t-2)\} = e^{-2(s+1)}/(s+1)$. Consequently, transforming the differential equation,

$$s^4x - s + 3s^2x + 2x = \frac{e^{-2(s+1)}}{s+1}$$

which gives

$$x = \frac{s}{(s^2+1)(s^2+2)} + \frac{e^{-2(s+1)}}{(s+1)(s^2+1)(s^2+2)}.$$

We now resolve into partial fractions. By inspection

$$\frac{1}{(s^2+1)(s^2+2)} = \frac{1}{s^2+1} - \frac{1}{s^2+2}$$

whereas

$$\frac{1}{(s+1)(s^2+1)(s^2+2)} = \frac{A}{s+1} + \frac{Bs+c}{s^2+1} + \frac{Ds+E}{s^2+2}$$

where A, B, C, D and E may be determined in the usual way. Multiply throughout by $(s+1)$ and let $s \to -1$, to get $A = \frac{1}{6}$. Next multiply by (s^2+1) and allow $s \to i$.

$$Bi + C = \frac{1}{(1+i)} = \frac{(1-i)}{2}$$

Since we could equally well let $s \to -i$, real and imaginary parts can be equated to give $B = -\frac{1}{2}$ $C = \frac{1}{2}$. Similarly, multiply throughout by (s^2+2) and let $s \to i\sqrt{2}$.

$$i\sqrt{2}D + E = \frac{1}{(1+i\sqrt{2})(-1)} = \frac{i\sqrt{2}-1}{3}$$

giving $D = \frac{1}{3}$, $E = -\frac{1}{3}$. Substituting these values into the expression for x we have

$$x = \frac{s}{s^2+1} - \frac{s}{s^2+2} + e^{-2(s+1)}\left(\frac{1}{6(s+1)} - \frac{s-1}{2(s^2+1)} + \frac{s-1}{3(s^2+2)}\right)$$

We invert noting that $\mathscr{L}^{-1}\{e^{-2s}f(s)\} = F(t-2)H(t-2)$, to obtain the solution

$$X = \cos t - \cos\sqrt{2}t + [e^{-(t-2)} - 3\cos(t-2) + 3\sin(t-2)$$
$$+ 2\cos\sqrt{2}(t-2) - \sqrt{2}\sin\sqrt{2}(t-2)]\frac{H(t-2)}{6e^2} \qquad \square$$

Problem 3.11   A particle of mass m moves in a straight line OX under the influence of (i) a restoring force mn^2X towards O, (ii) a damping force $2mk$

54

times the speed, (iii) a force $m F(t)$. Find the position $X = X(t)$ at any time $t > 0$, given that at $t = 0$ the particle is projected from $X = \alpha$ with speed β in the direction away from $X = 0$.

Solution. The equation of motion is obtained by equating mass times acceleration to total force; thus

$$mX'' = -mn^2X - 2mkX' + m F(t) \quad \text{or} \quad X'' + 2kX' + n^2X = F(t)$$

and initial conditions are $X(0) = \alpha$, $X'(0) = \beta$. Taking the Laplace transform of the whole equation with

$$\mathscr{L}\{X\} = x, \qquad \mathscr{L}\{X'\} = sx - \alpha, \qquad \mathscr{L}\{X''\} = s^2x - s\alpha - \beta$$

we get

$$s^2x - s\alpha - \beta + 2k(sx - \alpha) + n^2x = \mathscr{L}\{F(t)\} = f(s)$$

or, on rearranging,

$$x = \frac{s\alpha + 2k\alpha + \beta}{s^2 + 2ks + n^2} + \frac{f(s)}{s^2 + 2ks + n^2} \tag{i}$$

To evaluate the inverse we need to know the zeros of $s^2 + 2ks + n^2$. There are three cases to consider; since $s^2 + 2ks + n^2 = (s+k)^2 + n^2 - k^2$, the zeros are (1) *complex* if $n > k$, (2) *real and equal* if $n = k$, (3) *real and unequal* if $n < k$. We treat these three cases separately.

Case 1 $n > k$ *(under-damping).* Let $\sqrt{(n^2 - k^2)} = p$. When damping is small enough to make p real, the system is said to be *under-damped*. Then

$$s^2 + 2ks + n^2 \equiv (s+k)^2 + p^2 \quad \text{and}$$

$$\mathscr{L}^{-1}\left\{\frac{s+k}{(s+k)^2 + p^2}\right\} = e^{-kt}\cos pt \qquad \mathscr{L}^{-1}\left\{\frac{p}{(s+k)^2 + p^2}\right\} = e^{-kt}\sin pt$$

so that

$$\mathscr{L}^{-1}\left\{\frac{s\alpha + 2k\alpha + \beta}{(s+k)^2 + p^2}\right\} = e^{-kt}\left(\alpha \cos pt + \frac{k\alpha + \beta}{p}\sin pt\right).$$

This part of the solution for $X = X(t)$ is called the *free* oscillation (and is the whole solution when $F(t)$ is identically zero). The remaining part is

$$\mathscr{L}^{-1}\left\{\frac{f(s)}{(s+k)^2 + p^2}\right\} = F(t) * \frac{1}{p}e^{-kt}\sin pt = \frac{1}{p}\int_0^t e^{-k(t-u)}\sin p(t-u)F(u)\,du$$

by appeal to the convolution rule 12. This part is known as the *forced oscillation*. Therefore, the complete solution for this case is

$$\mathcal{L}^{-1}\{x\} = X = e^{-kt}\left(\alpha\cos pt + \frac{k\alpha+\beta}{p}\sin pt\right)$$

$$+\frac{1}{p}\int_0^t e^{-k(t-u)}\sin p(t-u)F(u)\,du$$

As $t \to \infty$ the solution is dominated by the forced oscillation.

Case 2 $n = k$ (*critical damping*). In this case the damping is just sufficient to give equality to the zeros, for here $s^2+2ks+n^2 = (s+k)^2$ so that

$$x = \frac{s\alpha+2k\alpha+\beta}{(s+k)^2}+\frac{f(s)}{(s+k)^2} = \frac{\alpha}{s+k}+\frac{k\alpha+\beta}{(s+k)^2}+\frac{f(s)}{(s+k)^2}$$

i.e. $\mathcal{L}^{-1}\{x\} = X = \alpha e^{-kt}+(k\alpha+\beta)te^{-kt}+\int_0^t e^{-k(t-u)}(t-u)F(u)\,du$

Case 3 $n < k$ (*over-damping*). Let $\sqrt{(k^2-n^2)} = q$. When damping is sufficiently large to make q real we say that the motion is *over-damped*. Then $s^2+2ks+n^2 = (s+k)^2-q^2$ and

$$\mathcal{L}^{-1}\left\{\frac{s+k}{(s+k)^2-q^2}\right\} = e^{-kt}\cosh qt \qquad \mathcal{L}^{-1}\left\{\frac{q}{(s+k)^2-q^2}\right\} = e^{-kt}\sinh qt$$

$$\mathcal{L}^{-1}\left\{\frac{s\alpha+2k\alpha+\beta}{(s+k)^2-q^2}\right\} = e^{-kt}\left(\alpha\cosh qt + \frac{k\alpha+\beta}{q}\sin qt\right)$$

which is the free oscillation and

$$\mathcal{L}^{-1}\left\{\frac{f(s)}{(s+k)^2-q^2}\right\} = F(t)*\frac{1}{q}e^{-kt}\sinh qt$$

$$= \frac{1}{q}\int_0^t e^{-k(t-u)}\sinh q(t-u)F(u)\,du$$

is the forced oscillation. The complete solution in this case is therefore

$$\mathcal{L}^{-1}\{x\} = X = e^{-kt}\left(\alpha\cosh qt + \frac{k\alpha+\beta}{q}\sinh qt\right)$$

$$+\frac{1}{q}\int_0^t e^{-k(t-u)}\sinh q(t-u)F(u)\,du$$

For large t the free oscillation, corresponding to $F(t) \equiv 0$, behaves like

$$\frac{1}{2}e^{-kt}\left(\alpha e^{qt}+\frac{k\alpha+\beta}{q}e^{qt}\right) = \frac{1}{2}e^{-(k-q)t}\left(\alpha+\frac{k\alpha+\beta}{q}\right)$$

which tends to zero as $t \to \infty$ because $q < k$. $\qquad\square$

3.3 Solution of Ordinary Differential Equations with Polynomial Coefficients

A method of solution using Rule 5 is illustrated in the following two problems.

Problem 3.12 Find $X = X(t)$ where $X'' + (2t-3)X' + 2X = 0$, $X(0) = 1$, $X'(0) = 3$.

Solution. With $\mathcal{L}\{X(t)\} = x(s)$, $\mathcal{L}\{X'\} = sx - 1$, $\mathcal{L}\{X''\} = s^2x - s - 3$ and by Rule 5 with $\mathcal{D} \equiv d/ds$, $\mathcal{L}\{tX'\} = -\mathcal{D}(sx-1)$. Hence the Laplace transform of the equation is

$$s^2x - s - 3 - (2\mathcal{D}+3)(sx-1) + 2x = 0$$

i.e.
$$\mathcal{D}x + (-\tfrac{1}{2}s + \tfrac{3}{2})x + \tfrac{1}{2} = 0$$

This is a linear equation in x and $\mathcal{D}x$ ($\equiv dx/ds$). The integrating factor is

$$R = \exp\left[\int(-\tfrac{1}{2}s + \tfrac{3}{2})\,ds\right] = e^{-\frac{1}{4}s^2 + \frac{3}{2}s}$$

Multiplying by R we get

$$\mathcal{D}(xe^{-\frac{1}{4}s^2 + \frac{3}{2}s}) = -\tfrac{1}{2}e^{-\frac{1}{4}s^2 + \frac{3}{2}s}$$

or
$$x = \tfrac{1}{2}e^{\frac{1}{4}s^2 - \frac{3}{2}s}\left[\int_s^\infty e^{-\frac{1}{4}u^2 + \frac{3}{2}u}\,du + c\right]$$

where c is an integration constant. Since by the first final s- limit Rule 9 $\lim\limits_{s\to\infty} x(s) = 0$ when $X(t) \in$ class $\mathcal{A}$, we must have $c = 0$ for finite $X(t)$, i.e.

$$x = \tfrac{1}{2}\int_s^\infty e^{-\frac{1}{4}(u^2 - s^2) + \frac{3}{2}(u-s)}\,du$$

To invert put $u = 2t + s$ so that

$$x = \int_0^\infty e^{-\frac{1}{4}(4t^2 + 4ts) + 3t}\,dt = \int_0^\infty e^{-st}e^{-t^2 + 3t}\,dt$$

By inspection the inverse Laplace transform is

$$X(t) = e^{-t^2 + 3t} \qquad \square$$

Problem 3.13 Solve $t^2X'' + t(2t+1)X' + (2t^2 + t - 1)X = 0$, $X(0) = 0$, $X'(0) = \tfrac{1}{2}$.

Solution. If $\mathcal{L}\{X(t)\} = x(s)$, then $\mathcal{L}\{X'\} = sx$, $\mathcal{L}\{X''\} = s^2x - \tfrac{1}{2}$ using Rule 5 where $\mathcal{D} \equiv d/ds$, $\mathcal{L}\{t^2X''\} = \mathcal{D}^2(s^2x - \tfrac{1}{2})$, $\mathcal{L}\{t(2t+1)X'\} = (2\mathcal{D}^2 - \mathcal{D})(sx)$, $\mathcal{L}\{(2t^2 + t - 1)X\} = (2\mathcal{D}^2 - \mathcal{D} - 1)x$ so that the transform of the whole differential equation is

$$\mathcal{D}^2(s^2x - \tfrac{1}{2}) + (2\mathcal{D}^2 - \mathcal{D})(sx) + (2\mathcal{D}^2 - \mathcal{D} - 1)x = 0$$

which reduces to

$$(s^2 + 2s + 2)\mathcal{D}^2x + 3(s+1)\mathcal{D}x = 0, \quad or$$

$$\frac{\mathcal{D}^2 x}{\mathcal{D}x} + \frac{3(s+1)}{(s+1)^2+1} = 0, \qquad \mathcal{D}^2 x \equiv d^2x/ds^2, \quad \mathcal{D}x \equiv dx/ds$$

Integrating

$$\ln \mathcal{D}x + \tfrac{3}{2}\ln[(s+1)^2+1] = \ln A \qquad A = \text{constant}$$

$$\mathcal{D}x = A[(s+1)^2+1]^{-\frac{3}{2}}$$

Integrating again

$$x = A(s+1)[(s+1)^2+1]^{-\frac{1}{2}} + B$$

where $B = $ constant. For finite X we must have $x \to 0$ as $s \to \infty$ (Rule 9) in which case $A+B = 0$ and

$$x = B(1-(s+1)[(s+1)^2+1]^{-\frac{1}{2}})$$

Using the result of Problem 1.20 with the shifting rule, Rule 3, the inverse is $X(t) = B e^{-t}J_1(t)$. Since $J'_1(0) = \tfrac{1}{2}$ and we are given $X'(0) = \tfrac{1}{2}$, it follows that $B = 1$ so that the required solution is $X(t) = e^{-t}J_1(t)$. $\qquad\blacksquare$

3.4 Simultaneous Ordinary Differential Equations These involve more than one dependent variable and a Laplace transform is needed for each variable. The procedure is to solve the simultaneous algebraic equations which arise for the transforms and then to invert using any convenient method.

Problem 3.14 Solve the equations

$$X' + Y' = 2Z, \tag{i}$$
$$Y' + Z' = 2X, \tag{ii}$$
$$Z' + X' = 2Y, \tag{iii}$$

given $X(0) = \alpha$, $Y(0) = \beta$, $Z(0) = \gamma$.

Solution. Let $\mathcal{L}\{X(t)\} = x(s)$, $\mathcal{L}\{Y(t)\} = y(s)$, $\mathcal{L}\{Z(t)\} = z(s)$. Then $\mathcal{L}\{X'\} = sx-\alpha$, $\mathcal{L}\{Y'\} = sy-\beta$, $\mathcal{L}\{Z'\} = sz- \gamma$. The transform of (i) is $sx-\alpha+sy-\beta = 2z$, i.e.

$$s(x+y)-2z = \alpha+\beta \tag{iv}$$

Similarly, (ii) and (iii) transform to

$$s(y+z)-2x = \beta+\gamma \tag{v}$$
$$s(z+x)-2y = \gamma+\alpha \tag{vi}$$

Adding,

$$(2s-2)(x+y+z) = 2\lambda \qquad \text{where } \lambda = \alpha+\beta+\gamma,$$

or

$$x+y+z = \frac{\lambda}{s-1}$$

Substituting in (iv) to solve for z,

$$s\left[\frac{\lambda}{(s-1)}-z\right]-2z = \alpha+\beta = \lambda-\gamma$$

i.e.
$$z = \frac{\lambda}{(s-1)(s+2)}+\frac{\gamma}{s+2} = \tfrac{1}{3}\lambda\left(\frac{1}{s-1}-\frac{1}{s+2}\right)+\frac{\gamma}{s+2}$$

Inverting, $Z = \tfrac{1}{3}\lambda e^t+(\gamma-\tfrac{1}{3}\lambda)e^{-2t}$. Similarly, $X = \tfrac{1}{3}\lambda e^t+(\alpha-\tfrac{1}{3}\lambda)e^{-2t}$
$Y = \tfrac{1}{3}\lambda e^t+(\beta-\tfrac{1}{3}\lambda)e^{-2t}$. $\qquad\qquad\qquad\qquad\qquad\qquad\square$

Problem 3.15   Solve the equations
$$X''+Y'+10X-2Y = 20\sin 2t$$
$$Y''+X'+2X-4Y = -20\cos 2t$$
where $X(0) = 0$, $X'(0) = 12$, $Y(0) = 11$, $Y'(0) = -9$.

Solution. With $\mathscr{L}\{X(t)\} = x(s)$, $\mathscr{L}\{Y(t)\} = y(s)$ we have $\mathscr{L}\{X'\} = sx$, $\mathscr{L}\{X''\} = s^2x-12$, $\mathscr{L}\{Y'\} = sy-11$, $\mathscr{L}\{Y''\} = s^2y-11s+9$.
Taking Laplace transforms of the given equations,
$$s^2x-12+sy-11+10x-2y = 40/(s^2+4)$$

and

$$s^2y-11s+9+sx+2x-4y = -20s/(s^2+4)$$

i.e.
$$(s^2+10)x+(s-2)y = \frac{40}{(s^2+4)}+23 \equiv f(s) \qquad\qquad\text{(i)}$$

$$(s+2)x+(s^2-4)y = -\frac{20s}{(s^2+4)}+11s-9 \equiv g(s) \qquad\qquad\text{(ii)}$$

Solving these linear equations for the transforms x and y,
$$x = \frac{(s^2-4)f-(s-2)g}{\Delta}, \qquad y = \frac{(s^2+10)g-(s+2)f}{\Delta} \qquad\text{(iii)}$$

where $\Delta = (s^2+10)(s^2-4)-(s+2)(s-2) = (s^2-4)(s^2+9)$.
Substituting for f and g in (i) and (ii), we get
$$x = \frac{40}{(s^2+4)(s^2+9)}+\frac{23}{s^2+9}+\frac{20s}{(s+2)(s^2+4)(s^2+9)}$$
$$-\frac{11s}{(s+2)(s^2+9)}+\frac{9}{(s+2)(s^2+9)} \qquad\text{(iv)}$$

By inspection, we have for arbitrary p and q,
$$\frac{1}{(s^2+p)(s^2+q)} = \frac{1}{p-q}\left(\frac{1}{s^2+q}-\frac{1}{s^2+p}\right), \qquad p \neq q \qquad\text{(v)}$$

and
$$\frac{1}{(s+a)(s^2+p)} = \frac{1}{p+a^2}\left(\frac{1}{s+a} - \frac{s-a}{s^2+p}\right) \qquad \text{(vi)}$$

so that

$$\frac{s}{(s+a)(s^2+p)} = \frac{1}{p+a^2}\left(\frac{s}{s+a} - \frac{s^2-as}{s^2+p}\right) = \frac{1}{p+a^2}\left[1 - \frac{a}{s+a} - 1 + \frac{p+as}{s^2+p}\right]$$

$$= \frac{1}{p+a^2}\left(-\frac{a}{s+a} + \frac{p+as}{s^2+p}\right) \qquad \text{(vii)}$$

Thus

$$\frac{1}{(s^2+4)(s^2+9)} = \frac{1}{5}\left(\frac{1}{s^2+4} - \frac{1}{s^2+9}\right) \qquad \frac{1}{(s^2+2)(s^2+9)} = \frac{1}{13}\left(\frac{1}{s+2} - \frac{s-2}{s^2+9}\right)$$

$$\frac{s}{(s+2)(s^2+9)} = \frac{1}{13}\left(\frac{2s+9}{s^2+9} - \frac{2}{s+2}\right)$$

Again writing $s/(s+2) = 1 - 2/(s+2)$ with further application of formulae (v), (vi), (vii),

$$\frac{s}{(s+2)(s^2+4)(s^2+9)} = \frac{1}{5}\left(1 - \frac{2}{s+2}\right)\left(\frac{1}{s^2+4} - \frac{1}{s^2+9}\right)$$

$$= \frac{1}{5}\left(\frac{1}{s^2+4} - \frac{1}{s^2+9} - \frac{2}{(s+2)(s^2+4)} + \frac{2}{(s+2)(s^2+9)}\right)$$

$$= \frac{1}{5}\left[\frac{1}{s^2+4} - \frac{1}{s^2+9} - \frac{2}{8}\left(\frac{1}{s+2} - \frac{s-2}{s^2+4}\right)\right.$$

$$\left. + \frac{2}{13}\left(\frac{1}{s+2} - \frac{s-2}{s^2+9}\right)\right]$$

$$= -\frac{1}{52(s+2)} + \frac{s+2}{20(s^2+4)} - \frac{2s+9}{65(s^2+9)}$$

Substituting these fractions into (iv) we find

$$x = 8\left(\frac{1}{s^2+4} - \frac{1}{s^2+9}\right) + \frac{23}{s^2+9} + 20\left(-\frac{1}{52(s+2)} + \frac{s+2}{20(s^2+4)} - \frac{2s+9}{65(s^2+9)}\right)$$

$$-\frac{11}{13}\left(\frac{2s+9}{s^2+9} - \frac{2}{s+2}\right) + \frac{9}{13}\left(\frac{1}{s+2} - \frac{s-2}{s^2+9}\right) = \frac{2}{s+2} + \frac{6-3s}{s^2+9} + \frac{s+10}{s^2+4}$$

of which the inverse is

$$X(t) = 2e^{-2t} + 2\sin 3t - 3\cos 3t + \cos 2t + 5\sin 2t \qquad \text{(viii)}$$

Similarly, from (i), (ii) and (iii),

$$y = \left(11s - 9 - \frac{20s}{s^2+4}\right)\frac{s^2+10}{(s^2-4)(s^2+9)} - \left(23 + \frac{40}{s^2+4}\right)\frac{s+2}{(s^2-4)(s^2+9)}$$

which reduces to the following partial fraction form:

$$y = \frac{7}{(s+2)} + \frac{3}{(s^2+9)} + \frac{4s+2}{(s^2+4)}$$

for which the inverse is $Y(t) = 7e^{-2t} + \sin 3t + \sin 2t + 4\cos 2t$. $\qquad\square$

3.5 Integral Equations of the Convolution Type   These are of the form

$$X(t) = G(t) + \int_0^t K(t-u)X(u)\, du$$

where $X(t)$ is the function to be determined when $G(t)$ and the *kernel* $K(t-u)$ are given. Because the integral is a convolution between functions K and X we may rewrite the relation in the form

$$X(t) = G(t) + K(t) * X(t)$$

With the notation $\mathscr{L}\{X(t)\} = x(s)$, $\mathscr{L}\{G(t)\} = g(s)$ and $\mathscr{L}\{K(t)\} = k(s)$, we take the Laplace transform of both sides and use Rule 12 to give $x(s) = g(s) + k(s)x(s)$ or

$$x(s) = g(s)/[1-k(s)]$$

from which $X(t)$ may now be determined by inversion.

An *integro-differential equation* contains derivatives of $X(t)$ in addition to the term in $X(t)$. Some types will also yield solutions using Laplace transform methods.

Problem 3.16   Solve the integral equation for $X(t)$,

$$X(t) = 7\sqrt{3}\sin\sqrt{3}t + 4\int_0^t \cos 2(t-u)X(u)\, du$$

Solution. Equating the Laplace transform of either side we have, using the convolution rule on the integral,

$$x = \frac{21}{(s^2+3)} + \frac{4sx}{(s^2+4)}$$

where $x = x(s) = \mathscr{L}\{X(t)\}$, i.e.

$$x[(s^2+3)(s^2+4) - 4s(s^2+3)] = 21(s^2+4)$$

or

$$x = \frac{21(s^2+4)}{(s^2+3)(s-2)^2} \equiv \frac{As+B}{s^2+3} + \frac{C}{s-2} + \frac{D}{(s-2)^2}$$

in terms of partial fractions, where A, B, C and D are to be determined. Now

$$D = \lim_{s\to 2}(s-2)^2 x = 24$$

$$i\sqrt{3}A + B = \lim_{s\to i\sqrt{3}}(s^2+3)x = \frac{21}{(i\sqrt{3}-2)^2} = \frac{21(-i\sqrt{3}-2)^2}{49} = \frac{3}{7}(1+4i\sqrt{3})$$

By equating real and imaginary parts, $A = \frac{12}{7}$ and $B = \frac{3}{7}$. To find C, put $s = 0$ in x and utilise the evaluated constants.

$$x(0) = 7 = \tfrac{1}{3}B - \tfrac{1}{2}C + \tfrac{1}{4}D = \tfrac{1}{7} - \tfrac{1}{2}C + 6$$

so that $C = -\frac{12}{7}$. Consequently,

$$x(s) = \frac{12s}{7(s^2+3)} + \frac{3}{7(s^2+3)} - \frac{12}{7(s-2)} + \frac{24}{(s-2)^2}$$

whose inversion is

$$X(t) = \frac{12}{7}\cos\sqrt{3}t + \frac{\sqrt{3}}{7}\sin\sqrt{3}t - \frac{12}{7}e^{2t} + 24te^{2t} \qquad \square$$

Problem 3.17 Solve for $X(t)$ the integral equation

$$p\int_0^t X(t-u)X(u)\,du = 2X(t) - \sin pt, \qquad p = \text{constant} \neq 0$$

Solution. Taking the Laplace transform where $x = x(s) = \mathscr{L}\{X(t)\}$,

$$px^2 = 2x - \frac{p}{s^2+p^2} \quad \text{i.e.} \quad p\left(x - \frac{1}{p}\right)^2 = \frac{1}{p} - \frac{p}{s^2+p^2} = \frac{s^2}{p(s^2+p^2)}.$$

Hence $x = \dfrac{1}{p}\left(1 \pm \dfrac{s}{\sqrt{(s^2+p^2)}}\right)$. Using Problems 1.7 and 1.20;

$$\mathscr{L}\{J_1(pt)\} = \frac{1}{p}\left(1 - \frac{s}{\sqrt{(s^2+p^2)}}\right), \qquad \mathscr{L}\{\delta(t)\} = 1$$

Therefore $X(t) = J_1(pt)$ or $X(t) = 2[\delta(t)/p] - J_1(pt)$. $\qquad \square$

Problem 3.18 Solve the following integro-differential equation subject to $X(0) = 0$;

$$5\int_0^t e^u \cos 2(t-u)X(u)\,du = e^t[X'(t) + X(t)] - 1$$

Solution. In order to apply the convolution rule we first multiply throughout by e^{-t} before taking the transform, for then

$$\int_0^t e^{-(t-u)}\cos 2(t-u)X(u)\,du = e^{-t}\cos 2t * X(t)$$

of which the Laplace transform is $(s+1)x/[(s+1)^2+4]$ where $x = x(s) = \mathscr{L}\{X(t)\}$. Therefore,

$$\frac{5(s+1)x}{[(s+1)^2+4]} = \mathscr{L}\{X'(t) + X(t) - e^{-t}\} = (s+1)x - \frac{1}{(s+1)}$$

since $X(0) = 0$. Hence

$$x = \frac{s^2+2s+5}{s(s+1)^2(s+2)} \equiv \frac{A}{s} + \frac{B}{s+2} + \frac{C}{s+1} + \frac{D}{(s+1)^2}$$

where A, B, C and D are constants to be determined. We have
$$A = \lim_{s \to 0} sx = \tfrac{5}{2}, B = \lim_{s \to -2} (s+2)x = -\tfrac{5}{2}, D = \lim_{s \to -1} (s+1)^2 x = -4.$$
Also $A+B+C = \lim_{s \to \infty} sx = 0$ giving $C = 0$. Consequently,
$$x(s) = \frac{5}{2s} - \frac{5}{2(s+2)} - \frac{4}{(s+1)^2}$$
of which the inverse is
$$X(t) = \tfrac{5}{2}(1-e^{-2t}) - 4te^{-t} \qquad \square$$

3.6 Linear Difference Equations A linear difference equation defines a linear relation between functions $X(t)$, $X(t+h)$, $X(t+2h), \ldots, X(t+nh)$ where h is a given constant and n a given integer. An example is
$$X(t+4h) - 5X(t+3h) - X(t) = F(t),$$
F being a known function. Alternatively, a linear difference equation may define a linear relation between the terms a_0, a_1, $a_2, \ldots$ of a sequence. For example, if $G(n)$ is known;
$$a_{n+5} - 4a_{n+2} - 6u_n = G(n)$$
defines one such relation. Equations of this type can be solved using the Laplace transform.

Problem 3.19 Solve $4X(t) - 5X(t-1) + X(t-2) = t^2$ for all $t > 0$ given that $X(t) = k$ when $t \leqslant 0$.

Solution. We take the Laplace transform of this relation and write $\mathcal{L}\{X(t)\} = x$ where $x = x(s)$. Thus,
$$4x - 5\mathcal{L}\{X(t-1)\} + \mathcal{L}\{X(t-2)\} = \mathcal{L}\{t^2\} = 2/s^3 \qquad \text{(ii)}$$
Now,
$$\mathcal{L}\{X(t-n)\} = \int_0^\infty e^{-st} X(t-n)\, dt = \int_{-n}^\infty e^{-s(u+n)} X(u)\, du \qquad (u = t-n)$$
$$= e^{-sn} \int_0^\infty e^{-su} X(u)\, du + e^{-sn} \int_{-n}^0 e^{-su} X(u)\, du$$
$$= e^{-sn}x + ke^{-sn} \int_{-n}^0 e^{-su}\, du \qquad (x(u) = k \quad \text{for } u \leqslant 0)$$
$$= e^{-sn}x + ke^{-sn} \left[-\frac{1}{s}e^{-su} \right]_{-n}^0 = e^{-sn}x + \frac{k}{s}(1-e^{-sn})$$
Hence (i) becomes
$$4x - 5e^{-s}x + e^{-2s}x = \frac{2}{s^3} + \frac{5k}{s}(1-e^{-s}) - \frac{k}{s}(1-e^{-2s})$$

63

$$x = \frac{k}{s} + \frac{2}{s^3(1-e^{-s})(4-e^{-s})} = \frac{k}{s} + \frac{2}{3s^3}\left(\frac{1}{1-e^{-s}} - \frac{1}{4-e^{-s}}\right)$$

$$= \frac{k}{s} + \frac{2}{3s^3}\left\{(1+e^{-s}+e^{-2s}+e^{-3s}+\ldots) - \frac{1}{4}\left(1+\frac{e^{-s}}{4}+\frac{e^{-2s}}{4^2}+\frac{e^{-3s}}{4^3}+\ldots\right)\right\}$$

$$= \frac{k}{s} + \frac{1}{2s^3} + \frac{2}{3}\sum_{n=1}^{\infty}(1-2^{2n+2})\frac{e^{-ns}}{s^3}$$

To invert this we use Rule 4. Then

$$X(t) = k + \tfrac{1}{4}t^2 + \tfrac{1}{3}\sum_{n=1}^{\infty}(1-2^{-2n-2})H(t-n)(t-n)^2$$

where $H(t-n) = 0$ for $t \leqslant n$ and $H(t-n) = 1$ for $t > n$ so that we may write

$$X(t) = k + \tfrac{1}{4}t^2 + \tfrac{1}{3}\sum_{n=1}^{[t]}(1-2^{-2n-2})(t-n)^2$$

where $[t]$ is the greatest integer not exceeding t. $\square$

Problem 3.20 Given a sequence of numbers a_r $(r = 0, 1, 2, \ldots)$, examine the function $X(t)$ defined by $X(t) = \sum_{n=0}^{\infty} a_n[H(t-n) - H(t-n-1)]$ where $H(u)$ denotes the Heaviside step function. Find expressions for $\mathscr{L}\{X(t)\}$ and $\mathscr{L}\{X(t+m)\}$ where m is a positive integer.

Solution. By definition,

$$H(t-n) = 0 \text{ if } t \leqslant n \qquad H(t-n-1) = 0 \text{ if } t \leqslant n+1$$
$$H(t-n) = 1 \text{ if } t > n \qquad H(t-n-1) = 1 \text{ if } t > n+1.$$

Hence

$$H(t-n) - H(t-n-1) = \begin{cases} 0, & t \leqslant n \\ 0, & t > n+1 \\ 1, & n < t \leqslant n+1 \end{cases}$$

Consequently $X(t) = a_n$ when $0 \leqslant n < t \leqslant n+1$. Again, for $t > 0$,

$$X(t+m) = \sum_{p=0}^{\infty} a_p[H(t+m-p) - H(t+m-p-1)]$$

$$= \sum_{n=-m}^{\infty} a_{n+m}[H(t-n) - H(t-n-1)]$$

where $p = n+m$. However, $H(u) = 0$ for $u \leqslant 0$, and since $t > 0$ we can omit negative values of n in the summation and write

$$X(t+m) = \sum_{n=0}^{\infty} a_{n+m}[H(t-n)-H(t-n-1)]$$

The Laplace transform of $X(t)$ is

$$\mathcal{L}\{X(t)\} = x(s) = \sum_{n=0}^{\infty} a_n[\mathcal{L}\{H(t-n)\} - \mathcal{L}\{H(t-n-1)\}]$$

$$= \sum_{n=0}^{\infty} a_n \left[\frac{e^{-ns}}{s} - \frac{e^{-(n+1)s}}{s} \right]$$

i.e.
$$x(s) = \frac{1}{s}(1-e^{-s}) \sum_{n=0}^{\infty} a_n e^{-ns} = \frac{1}{s}(1-e^{-s})\sigma(s)$$

where $\sigma(s) = \sum_{n=0}^{\infty} a_n e^{-ns}$. To find the Laplace transform of $X(t+m)$ we have

$$\mathcal{L}\{X(t+m)\} = \int_0^{\infty} e^{-st}X(t+m)\, dt$$

$$= \int_m^{\infty} e^{-s(u-m)}X(u)\, du \qquad (u = t+m)$$

$$= e^{ms}\left[x(s) - \int_0^m e^{-su}X(u)\, du\right]$$

Now if $n \leqslant m$,
$$\int_0^m e^{-st}H(t-n)\, dt = \int_n^m e^{-st}\, dt = (e^{-ns}-e^{-ms})/s$$

whereas for $n > m$ the value of the integral on the left is zero. Similarly for $n+1 \leqslant m$,

$$\int_0^m e^{-st}H(t-n-1)\, dt = (e^{-(n+1)s}-e^{-ms})/s$$

and so

$$\mathcal{L}\{X(t+m)\} = e^{ms}\left[x(s) - s^{-1}\sum_{n=0}^{m-1} a_n(e^{-ns}-e^{-(n+1)s})\right]$$

$$= s^{-1}e^{ms}(1-e^{-s})\left[\sigma(s) - \sum_{n=0}^{m-1} a_n e^{-ns}\right]. \qquad \square$$

Problem 3.21 Use the function $X(t)$ defined in Problem 3.20 to solve the difference equation $a_{n+2} - 5a_{n+1} + 4_n^a = 0$, $\qquad n = 0, 1, 2, \ldots$.

Solution. Using the theory in the solution to Problem 3.20 we have, multiplying the given relation throughout by the factor $H(t-n) - H(t-n-1)$ and summing,

$$X(t+2) - 5X(t+1) + 4X(t) = 0$$

Taking the Laplace transform and dividing out the common factor $(1-e^{-s})/s$,

$$e^{2s}[\sigma(s)-a_0-a_1e^{-s}]-5[\sigma(s)-a_0]+4\sigma(s) = 0,$$

i.e.

$$\sigma(s) = \frac{a_1e^s+a_0(e^{2s}-5e^s)}{e^{2s}-5e^s+4} = \frac{Ae^s}{e^s-4}+\frac{Be^s}{e^s-1}$$

where $A+B = a_0$ and $A+4B = 5a_0-a_1$ giving $A = \frac{1}{3}(a_1-a_0)$, $B = \frac{1}{3}(4a_0-a_1)$. Expanding $\sigma(s)$ in powers of e^{-s} we can evaluate a_n as the coefficient of e^{-ns}, since $\sigma(s) = \sum a_n e^{-ns}$ by definition. Therefore,

$$\sigma(s) = A(1-4e^{-s})^{-1}+B(1-e^{-s})^{-1}$$

$$= A\sum_{n=0}^{\infty}(4e^{-s})^n+B\sum_{n=0}^{\infty}(e^{-s})^n = \sum_{n=0}^{\infty}(A.4^n+B)e^{-ns}$$

i.e. $a_n = A.4^n+B = \frac{1}{3}(a_1-a_0)4^n+\frac{1}{3}(4a_0-a_1)$

a_0 and a_1 being arbitrary. $\square$

EXERCISES

1.   Use Laplace transforms to prove that $\int_0^{\infty}(\cos xt/\sqrt{t})\,dt = \sqrt{(\pi/2x)}$, $x > 0$;
$\int_0^{\frac{1}{2}\pi}\sin(2t\sin^2\theta)\,d\theta = \frac{1}{2}\sin t\,J_0(t); \int_0^{\infty}e^{-tx^2}/(1+x^2)\,dx = \frac{1}{2}\pi e^t\mathrm{erf}(\sqrt{t})$, $t > 0$

Solve for $X = X(t)$:

2.   (i) $X''+6X'+25X = F(t)$, $X(0) = X'(0) = 0$
      (ii) $X''+6X'+13X = e^{2t}(13\sin 4t+40\cos 4t)$, $X(0) = X'(0) = 1$.

3. $tX''+3X'+tX = 0$, $X(0) = \frac{1}{2}$.

Solve for $X = X(t)$ and $Y = Y(t)$:

4. $2X''+Y'-2X-Y = -\cos t-\sin t$, $X(0) = 4$, $X'(0) = \frac{3}{2}$;
      $2Y''-2X'+Y-2X = 3\cos t+4\sin t$, $Y(0) = 6$, $Y'(0) = 5$.

5. $X+Y' = e^{-t}$, $3X+X' = Y-3Y'$, $X(0) = 1 = Y(0)$.

6.   Solve for a_n, $a_{n+2} = a_n+a_{n+1}$, $n = 0,1,2,\ldots$, where $a_0 = 0$, $a_1 = 1$.

Solve for $X = X(t)$:

7. $F(t) = \int_0^t(t-u)^{-p}X'(u)\,du$, $0 < p < 1$.

8. $X(t)-X(t-a) = H(t)e^t$, $a > 0$, $X(t) = 0$ for $t < 0$.

Chapter 4

Inversion Theorem

Up to now except in one or two problems the parameter s has been considered to be real. If we extend the definition of the Laplace transform integral to complex values of $s = \sigma + i\omega$ we can express the inversion of $f(s)$ as an integral in the complex s-plane.

4.1 The Inversion Theorem Given that $F(t) \in$ class $\mathscr{A}$ with $\mathscr{L}\{F(t)\} = f(s)$, then it can be shown that when $t > 0$

$$F(t) = \frac{1}{2\pi i} \int_{\sigma - i\infty}^{\sigma + i\infty} e^{st} f(s) \, ds, \qquad s = \sigma + i\omega$$

This integral is the line integral in the s-plane parallel to the imaginary axis, and displaced from it a distance σ so chosen as to contain all the singular points of $f(s)$ to the left of the line.

The evaluation of the integral can be accomplished by considering the integration of $e^{st}f(s)$ around a closed contour C of which the line $\mathrm{Re}\,s = \sigma$ = constant forms a part (see Fig. 4.1). This contour C consists of part of the circle $|s| = R$ of radius R with centre at $s = 0$ for $\alpha \leqslant \mathrm{Arg}\,s \leqslant 2\pi - \alpha$ and the line $\mathrm{Re}\,s = \sigma$ for $-\alpha \leqslant \mathrm{Arg}\,s \leqslant \alpha$ where $\cos\alpha = \sigma/R$.

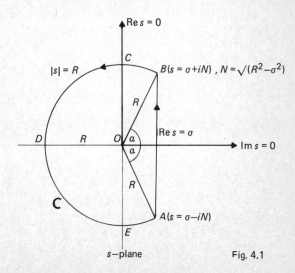

s—plane   Fig. 4.1

Suppose that, in the first instance, there are in all n singular points of the integrand at points $s = s_r$, $(r = 1, 2, \ldots, n)$ all contained within the contour C so defined. By the Cauchy residue theorem we have

$$\int_\Omega e^{st}f(s)\,ds + \int_{AB} e^{st}f(s)\,ds = 2\pi i \sum_{r=1}^{n} \mathcal{R}\big[e^{st}f(s)\big]_{s=s_r}$$

where Ω is the curved portion of C, AB is the straight portion and $\mathcal{R}[\ldots]_{s=s_r}$ denotes the residue at $s = s_r$. If for large R, $|f(s)| < MR^{-m}$, $M > 0, m > 0$, then the integral over Ω tends to zero for $t > 0$ as $R \to \infty$ and we are left with the evaluation of the infinite straight line integral in terms of the sum of the residues within C. To prove this, consider separately the integrals I_{BC} and I_{CD} over the arcs BC and CD respectively.

$$I_{BC} = \int_\alpha^{\frac{1}{2}\pi} e^{tRe^{i\theta}}f(s)\,Rie^{i\theta}\,d\theta$$

since $|e^{tR\cos\theta}| < e^{\sigma t}$ and $|e^{itR\sin\theta}| = 1$,

$$|I_{BC}| < MR^{-m+1}e^{\sigma t}\int_\alpha^{\frac{1}{2}\pi} d\theta = MR^{-m+1}e^{\sigma t}\sin^{-1}(\sigma/R)$$

i.e. $\lim_{R \to \infty} I_{BC} = 0$ when $m > 0$. Again,

$$|I_{CD}| < MR^{-m+1}\int_{\frac{1}{2}\pi}^{\pi} e^{Rt\cos\theta}\,d\theta = MR^{-m+1}\int_0^{\frac{1}{2}\pi} e^{-Rt\sin\theta}\,d\theta$$

$$< MR^{-m+1}\int_0^{\frac{1}{2}\pi} e^{-2Rt\theta/\pi}\,d\theta$$

$$\text{since } 1 > \frac{\sin\theta}{\theta} \leqslant \frac{2}{\pi} \text{ if } 0 < \theta \leqslant \tfrac{1}{2}\pi$$

$$= M\pi R^{-m}/(2t)$$

Hence, $\lim_{R \to \infty} |I_{CD}| = 0$. Similarly the integrals over the arc DE and EA vanish when $R \to \infty$ so that

$$\lim_{R \to \infty} \int_\Omega e^{st}f(s)\,ds = 0,$$

and since $N = \sqrt{(R^2 - \sigma^2)}$

$$\frac{1}{2\pi i}\lim_{N \to \infty}\int_{\sigma-iN}^{\sigma+iN} e^{st}f(s)\,ds = \frac{1}{2\pi i}\int_{\sigma-i\infty}^{\sigma+i\infty} e^{st}f(s)\,ds = \sum_{r=1}^{n} \mathcal{R}\big[e^{st}f(s)\big]_{s=s_r}$$

In the case when $f(s)$ has an infinite number of isolated poles and $f(s) = O(|s|^{-m})$, $m > 0$, the result in the limit is

$$\frac{1}{2\pi i}\int_{\sigma-i\infty}^{\sigma+i\infty} e^{st}f(s)\,ds = \sum_{r=1}^{\infty} \mathcal{R}\big[e^{st}f(s)\big]_{s=s_r}$$

The integral exists, by hypothesis, and so the series is convergent.

68

Problem 4.1 Use the inversion theorem to find
$$\mathcal{L}^{-1}\left\{\frac{s^3+2s^2+1}{s^2(s^2+1)}\right\}.$$

Solution. This function is analytic everywhere except for a double pole at $s=0$ and simple poles at $s=\pm i$. At $s=0$, the residue of $e^{st}f(s)$ is

$$\lim_{s\to 0}\left\{\frac{d}{ds}[s^2 e^{st}f(s)]\right\} = \left\{\frac{d}{ds}\left[\frac{e^{st}(s^3+2s^2+1)}{s^2+1}\right]\right\}_{s=0}$$

$$=\left\{\frac{te^{st}(s^3+2s^2+1)}{s^2+1}+\frac{e^{st}(3s^2+4s)}{s^2+1}-\frac{2se^{st}(s^3+2s^2+1)}{(s^2+1)^2}\right\}_{s=0} = t$$

At $s=i$, the residue is

$$\lim_{s\to i}[(s-i)e^{st}f(s)] = \left[\frac{e^{st}(s^3+2s^2+1)}{s^2(s+i)}\right]_{s=i} = \frac{e^{it}(-i-1)}{(-1)(2i)} = \tfrac{1}{2}(1-i)e^{it}$$

Moreover, by changing the sign of i it follows that the residue at $s=-i$ is $\tfrac{1}{2}(1+i)e^{-it}$. Hence, summing over residues and noting that for large $|s|$, $f(s)=O(1/s)$ we have

$$\mathcal{L}^{-1}\left\{\frac{s^3+2s^2+1}{s^2(s^2+1)}\right\} = t+\tfrac{1}{2}(1-i)e^{it}+\tfrac{1}{2}(1+i)e^{-it} = t+\cos t+\sin t \qquad \square$$

Problem 4.2 Find the inverse of $f(s) = \sinh sx/(s^2\sinh sa)$ where, $0 < x < a$.

Solution. The function $f(s)$ has poles at $s=0$ and possibly also at values of s for which $\sinh sa = 0$, i.e. at points
$$s = s_r = ir\pi/a, \qquad r = 0, \pm 1, \pm 2,\dots$$
Near $s=0$, $\sinh sx = sx+O(s^3)$, $\sinh sa = sa+O(s^3)$ so that $f(s) = x/(sa^2)+O(1)$, i.e. $s=0$ is a double pole.

The poles $s=s_r$ for $r = \pm 1, \pm 2,\dots$ are simple. The residue at $s=0$ is
$$R_0 = \lim_{s\to 0}\frac{d}{ds}[s^2 e^{st}f(s)] = \lim_{s\to 0}\frac{d}{ds}\left[e^{st}\frac{\sinh sx}{\sinh sa}\right]$$

But
$$\frac{\sinh sx}{\sinh sa} = \frac{sx(1+\tfrac{1}{6}s^2 x^2+\dots)}{sa(1+\tfrac{1}{6}s^2 a^2+\dots)} = \frac{x}{a}(1+\tfrac{1}{6}s^2(x^2-a^2)+\dots)$$

for small s hence
$$R_0 = \lim_{s\to 0}\frac{x}{a}\frac{d}{ds}[e^{st}(1+As^2+\dots)] \qquad A = \tfrac{1}{6}(x^2-a^2)$$
$$= \frac{x}{a}\lim_{s\to 0}[te^{st}(1+As^2+\dots)+e^{st}(2As+\dots)] = \frac{xt}{a}$$

69

The residue at $s = s_r = ir\pi/a$ is

$$R_r = \lim_{s \to ir\pi/a} \left[(s - ir\pi/a)e^{st}f(s)\right]$$

$$= \lim_{\delta \to 0} \left[\delta e^{t(\delta + ir\pi/a)}f(\delta + ir\pi/a)\right] \qquad (\delta = s - ir\pi/a)$$

$$= \lim_{\delta \to 0} \frac{e^{ir\pi t/a}\delta e^{t\delta}\sinh(\delta x + ir\pi x/a)}{[(\delta + ir\pi/a)^2\sinh(\delta a + ir\pi)]}$$

For small δ,

$$\sinh(\delta a + ir\pi) = (-1)^r\sinh \delta a = (-1)^r\delta a + O(\delta^3)$$

and

$$\sinh\left(\delta x + \frac{ir\pi x}{a}\right) = \sinh \delta x \cos \frac{r\pi x}{a} + i \cosh \delta x \sin \frac{r\pi x}{a}$$

$$= i \sin \frac{r\pi x}{a} + O(\delta)$$

Hence

$$R_r = e^{ir\pi t/a} \lim_{\delta \to 0} \frac{\delta e^{t\delta}[i\sin(r\pi x/a) + O(\delta)]}{[-(r^2\pi^2/a^2) + O(\delta)][(-1)^r\delta a + O(\delta^3)]}$$

$$= \frac{a}{\pi^2}(-1)^{r+1} \frac{i\sin(r\pi x/a)}{r^2} e^{ir\pi t/a}$$

Similarly the residue R_{-r} at $s = -ir\pi/a$ is

$$\frac{a}{\pi^2}(-1)^{r+1} \frac{(-i)\sin(r\pi x/a)}{r^2} e^{-ir\pi t/a}$$

Therefore, since, $e^{ir\pi t/a} - e^{-ir\pi t/a} = 2i\sin(r\pi t/a)$

$$R_r + R_{-r} = \frac{2a}{\pi^2}\frac{(-1)^r}{r^2}\sin\frac{r\pi x}{a}\sin\frac{r\pi t}{a}$$

Using the inversion theorem, and assuming that the integral over Ω (of Section 4.1) tends to zero for infinite radius,

$$\mathscr{L}^{-1}\left\{\frac{\sinh sx}{s^2\sinh sa}\right\} = R_0 + \sum_{r=1}^{\infty} (R_r + R_{-r})$$

$$= \frac{xt}{a} + \frac{2a}{\pi^2}\sum_{r=1}^{\infty} \frac{(-1)^r}{r^2}\sin\frac{r\pi x}{a}\sin\frac{r\pi t}{a} \qquad \square$$

4.2 The Inversion Theorem when $f(s)$ has a Branch Point In the case when $f(s)$ has a branch point at $s = 0$, say, we have to exclude this point from the region of integration and therefore the contour in Fig. 4.1 has to be modified. The new contour is illustrated in Fig. 4.2, where the original one

70

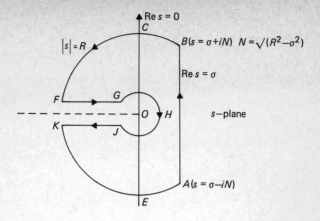

Fig. 4.2

has been cut from O to D along the negative real axis and the point O excluded by the bypass along the small circular path $|s| = \varepsilon$. After cutting, ε is to be allowed to tend to zero. The procedure is illustrated in the ensuing problems.

Problem 4.3 Find $\mathscr{L}^{-1}\{se^{-a\sqrt{s}}/(s^2+p^2)\}$, $a > 0$.

Solution. The required inverse is given by

$$\left(\frac{1}{2\pi i}\right)\int_{\sigma-i\infty}^{\sigma+i\infty} e^{st}f(s)ds, \qquad f(s) \equiv \frac{se^{-a\sqrt{s}}}{s^2+p^2} \tag{i}$$

The integrand has simple poles at $s = \pm ip$ and a branch point at $s = 0$.

Consider the integral of $e^{st}f(s)$ over the contour C of Fig. 4.2. In order to enclose the two simple poles at $s = \pm ip$ we must choose $R > p$. We split this integral into six component integrals as indicated below and then we consider each separately. Consequently,

$$\int_c e^{st}f(s)\,ds = \left(\int_{AB} + \int_{BCF} + \int_{FG} + \int_{GHJ} + \int_{JK} + \int_{KEA}\right)e^{st}f(s)\,ds \tag{ii}$$

First, we have $\int_c e^{st}f(s)\,ds = 2\pi i(R_+ + R_-)$ where R_+ and R_- are the residues of $e^{st}f(s)$ at $s = ip$ and $s = -ip$ respectively. The first of these residues is

$$R_+ = \lim_{s \to ip}\left[(s-ip)\frac{se^{st-a\sqrt{s}}}{s^2+p^2}\right] = \lim_{s \to ip}\left[\frac{se^{st-a\sqrt{s}}}{s+ip}\right]$$

Since $s = ip = pe^{\frac{1}{2}\pi i}$, then $\sqrt{s} = \sqrt{pe^{\frac{1}{2}\pi i}} = (1+i)\sqrt{(\frac{1}{2}p)}$. Therefore

$$R_+ = \tfrac{1}{2}e^{-a\sqrt{(\frac{1}{2}p)}}e^{i(pt-a\sqrt{(\frac{1}{2}p))}}$$

Similarly, by changing the sign of i

$$R_- = \tfrac{1}{2}e^{-a\sqrt{(\frac{1}{2}p)}}e^{-i(pt-a\sqrt{(\frac{1}{2}p))}},$$

so that

$$\int_c e^{st}f(s)\,ds = 2\pi i(R_+ + R_-) = 2\pi i e^{-a\sqrt{(\frac{1}{2}p)}}\cos\{pt-a\sqrt{(\tfrac{1}{2}p)}\} \qquad \text{(iii)}$$

Considering each of the integrals on the right-hand side of equation (ii) in turn, we have:

(a) $$\int_{AB} = \int_{\sigma-iN}^{\sigma+iN} e^{st}f(s)\,ds \qquad \text{(iv)}$$

(b) On BCF $s = Re^{i\theta}$, $\alpha \leqslant \theta \leqslant \pi$,

$$\int_{BCF} e^{st}f(s)\,ds \to 0 \text{ as } R \to \infty$$

(c) On FG $s = \sigma e^{\pi i} = -\sigma$, $\sqrt{s} = \sqrt{\sigma}e^{\frac{1}{2}\pi i} = i\sqrt{\sigma}$. As s moves from $-R$ to $-\varepsilon$, σ reduces from R to ε, therefore,

$$\int_{FG} e^{st}f(s)\,ds = \int_{-R}^{-\varepsilon} e^{st-a\sqrt{s}}\frac{s\,ds}{s^2+p^2} = -\int_{\varepsilon}^{R} e^{-\sigma t-ai\sqrt{\sigma}}\frac{\sigma\,d\sigma}{\sigma^2+p^2} \qquad \text{(v)}$$

(d) On GHJ, $s = \varepsilon e^{i\theta}$ where θ decreases from π to $-\pi$. Hence

$$\int_{GHJ} e^{st}f(s)\,ds = \int_{-\pi}^{\pi} e^{t\varepsilon e^{i\theta}-a\sqrt{\varepsilon}e^{\frac{1}{2}i\theta}} i\varepsilon^2 e^{2i\theta}(\varepsilon^2 e^{2i\theta}+p^2)^{-1}\,d\theta$$

The limit as $\varepsilon \to 0$ can be taken under the integral. When $p \neq 0$, this integral behaves like ε^2 where ε is small and therefore

$$\int_{GHJ} e^{st}f(s)\,ds \to 0 \text{ as } \varepsilon \to 0$$

(e) On JK $s = \sigma e^{-\pi i} = -\sigma$, $\sqrt{s} = \sqrt{\sigma}e^{-\frac{1}{2}\pi i} = -i\sqrt{\sigma}$, i.e.

$$\int_{JK} e^{st}f(s)\,ds = \int_{-\varepsilon}^{-R} e^{st-a\sqrt{s}}\frac{s\,ds}{s^2+p^2} = \int_{\varepsilon}^{R} e^{-\sigma t+ai\sqrt{\sigma}}\frac{\sigma\,d\sigma}{\sigma^2+p^2} \qquad \text{(vi)}$$

(f) On KEA, $s = Re^{i\theta}$, $\pi \leqslant \theta \leqslant 2\pi-\alpha$. Hence $\int_{KEA} e^{st}f(s)\,ds \to 0$ as $R \to \infty$.

Combining (i) to (vi) and allowing $R \to \infty$ and $\varepsilon \to 0$

$$(2\pi i)^{-1}\int_c e^{st}f(s)\,ds = e^{-a\sqrt{(\frac{1}{2}p)}}\cos\{pt-a\sqrt{(\tfrac{1}{2}p)}\}$$

$$= \frac{1}{2\pi i}\int_{\sigma-i\infty}^{\sigma+i\infty} e^{st}f(s)\,ds - \frac{1}{2\pi i}\int_0^{\infty} e^{-\sigma t-ai\sqrt{\sigma}}\frac{\sigma\,d\sigma}{\sigma^2+p^2}$$

$$+ \frac{1}{2\pi i}\int_0^{\infty} e^{-\sigma t+ai\sqrt{\sigma}}\frac{\sigma\,d\sigma}{\sigma^2+p^2}$$

$$= \frac{1}{2\pi i} \int_{\sigma - i\infty}^{\sigma + i\infty} e^{st} f(s)\, ds + \frac{1}{\pi} \int_0^\infty e^{-\sigma t} \sin(a\sqrt{\sigma}) \frac{\sigma\, d\sigma}{\sigma^2 + p^2}$$

whence

$$F(t) = \mathscr{L}^{-1}\{f(s)\} = \frac{1}{2\pi i} \int_{\sigma - i\infty}^{\sigma + i\infty} e^{st} f(s)\, ds$$

$$= e^{-a\sqrt{(\frac{1}{2}p)}} \cos\{pt - a\sqrt{(\tfrac{1}{2}p)}\} - \frac{1}{\pi} \int_0^\infty e^{-\sigma t} \sin(a\sqrt{\sigma}) \frac{\sigma\, d\sigma}{\sigma^2 + p^2} \qquad \square$$

Problem 4.4 Using the results of Problem 4.3, deduce the following:

(i) $\mathscr{L}^{-1}\{e^{-a\sqrt{s}}/s\} = \mathrm{erfc}(a/\sqrt{(4t)})$

(ii) $\mathscr{L}^{-1}\{e^{-a\sqrt{s}}/\sqrt{s}\} = e^{-a^2/4t}/\sqrt{(\pi t)}$

(iii) $\mathscr{L}^{-1}\{e^{-a\sqrt{s}}\} = \frac{1}{2} a e^{-a^2/4t}/\sqrt{(\pi t^3)}$

(iv) $\mathscr{L}^{-1}\{\sqrt{s}\, e^{-a\sqrt{s}}\} = \frac{1}{4}(a^2 - 2t)e^{-a^2/4t}/\sqrt{(\pi t^5)}$

(v) $\mathscr{L}^{-1}\{e^{-a\sqrt{s}}/(s + b\sqrt{s})\} = e^{ab + b^2 t}\mathrm{erfc}(b\sqrt{t} + \frac{1}{2}a/\sqrt{t})$

Solution. (i) We let $p \to 0$ in Problem 4.3 so that

$$\mathscr{L}^{-1}\{e^{-a\sqrt{s}}/s\} = 1 - \frac{1}{\pi} \int_0^\infty e^{-\sigma t} \sin(a\sqrt{\sigma}) \frac{d\sigma}{\sigma} = 1 - \frac{2J}{\pi}$$

where $J = \int_0^\infty e^{-u^2 t}(\sin au/u)\, du$ and $\sigma = u^2$

To evaluate J we first differentiate with respect to a under the integral sign. This gives

$$\frac{\partial J}{\partial a} = \int_0^\infty e^{-u^2 t}\cos au\, du = I(a, t), \quad \text{say}$$

Differentiating again and integrating by parts with respect to u, we have

$$\frac{\partial I}{\partial a} = -\int_0^\infty u e^{-u^2 t}\sin au\, du = \left[\frac{1}{2t} e^{-u^2 t}\sin au\right]_0^\infty - \frac{1}{2t}\int_0^\infty a e^{-u^2 t}\cos au\, du$$

giving $\partial I/\partial a = -aI/2t$. Integrating this differential equation, $I(a, t) = A(t)e^{-a^2/4t}$ where $A(t)$ is to be determined. Now

$$I(0, t) = A(t) = \int_0^\infty e^{-u^2 t}\, du = \left(\frac{1}{\sqrt{t}}\right)\int_0^\infty e^{-w^2}\, dw = \frac{1}{2}\sqrt{\left(\frac{\pi}{t}\right)}$$

so that

$$I(a, t) = \frac{1}{2}\sqrt{(\pi/t)}e^{-a^2/4t} = \frac{\partial J}{\partial a}$$

Integrating again using $J(0, t) = 0$,

$$J(a, t) = \frac{1}{2}\sqrt{(\pi/t)}\int_0^a e^{-v^2/4t}\, dv = \sqrt{\pi}\int_0^{a\sqrt{(4t)}} e^{-w^2}\, dw = \frac{1}{2}\pi\, \mathrm{erf}(a/\sqrt{(4t)}).$$

73

Finally, we obtain

$$\mathscr{L}^{-1}\{e^{-a\sqrt{s}}/s\} = 1 - 2J/\pi = 1 - \mathrm{erf}(a/\sqrt{(4t)}) = \mathrm{erfc}(a/\sqrt{(4t)})$$

(ii) $$\mathscr{L}^{-1}\left\{\frac{e^{-a\sqrt{s}}}{\sqrt{s}}\right\} = -\frac{\partial}{\partial a}\mathscr{L}^{-1}\left\{\frac{e^{-a\sqrt{s}}}{s}\right\} = \frac{2}{\pi}\frac{\partial J}{\partial a} = \frac{2}{\pi}I = \frac{e^{-a^2/4t}}{\sqrt{(\pi t)}}$$

(iii) $$\mathscr{L}^{-1}\{e^{-a\sqrt{s}}\} = \frac{\partial}{\partial a}\mathscr{L}^{-1}\left\{\frac{e^{-a\sqrt{s}}}{\sqrt{s}}\right\} = -\frac{\partial}{\partial a}\left(\frac{e^{-a^2/4t}}{\sqrt{(\pi t)}}\right) = \frac{1}{2}\frac{ae^{-a^2/4t}}{\sqrt{(\pi t^3)}}$$

(iv) $$\mathscr{L}^{-1}\{\sqrt{s}\,e^{-a\sqrt{s}}\} = -\frac{\partial}{\partial a}\mathscr{L}^{-1}\{e^{-a\sqrt{s}}\} = -\frac{\partial}{\partial a}\left(\frac{ae^{-a^2/4t}}{2\sqrt{(\pi t^3)}}\right)$$

$$= \frac{(a^2-2t)}{4}\cdot\frac{e^{-a^2/4t}}{\sqrt{(\pi t^5)}}$$

(v) Here we note that

$$\frac{1}{s+b\sqrt{s}} = \frac{b\sqrt{s}-s}{s(b^2-s)} = \frac{1}{b}\left(\frac{1}{\sqrt{s}}+\frac{b-\sqrt{s}}{s-b^2}\right)$$

so that

$$b\mathscr{L}^{-1}\left\{\frac{e^{-a\sqrt{s}}}{s+b\sqrt{s}}\right\} = \mathscr{L}^{-1}\left\{\frac{e^{-a\sqrt{s}}}{\sqrt{s}}\right\} + \mathscr{L}^{-1}\left\{\frac{be^{-a\sqrt{s}}}{s-b^2}\right\} - \mathscr{L}^{-1}\left\{\frac{\sqrt{s}\,e^{-a\sqrt{s}}}{s-b^2}\right\}$$

$$= I_1 + I_2 - I_3 \quad \text{(say)}$$

where

$$I_1 = \frac{e^{-a^2/4t}}{\sqrt{(\pi t)}}$$

using (ii);

$$I_2 = \int_0^t \left[\frac{bae^{-a^2/4u}}{2\sqrt{(\pi u^3)}}\right]e^{b^2(t-u)}\,du$$

using (iii), $\mathscr{L}^{-1}\{1/(s-b^2)\} = e^{b^2t}$ and the convolution rule. Again

$$I_3 = \int_0^t \left[\frac{(a^2-2u)e^{-a^2/4u}}{4\sqrt{(\pi u^5)}}\right]e^{b^2(t-u)}\,du,$$

using (iv), $\mathscr{L}^{-1}\{1/(s-b^2)\} = e^{b^2t}$ and the convolution rule.
Adding, we find

$$b\sqrt{\pi}\,\mathscr{L}^{-1}\left\{\frac{e^{-a\sqrt{s}}}{s+b\sqrt{s}}\right\} = \frac{e^{-a^2/4t}}{t^{\frac{1}{2}}} + e^{b^2t}\int_0^t\left(\frac{ab+1}{2u^{\frac{3}{2}}}-\frac{a^2}{4u^{\frac{5}{2}}}\right)e^{-a^2/4u-b^2u}\,du$$

Now eliminate the term within the integral involving the highest power of u, namely, $-(a^2/4u^{\frac{5}{2}})$ by using the identity

$$\left(-\frac{a^2}{4u^{\frac{5}{2}}}+\frac{1}{2u^{\frac{3}{2}}}+\frac{b^2}{u^{\frac{1}{2}}}\right)e^{-a^2/4u-b^2u} \equiv -\frac{d}{du}\left(\frac{e^{-a^2/4u-b^2u}}{u^{\frac{1}{2}}}\right)$$

74

or, on integration and the introduction of the factor $e^{b^2 t}$

$$e^{b^2 t} \int_0^t \left(-\frac{a^2}{4u^{\frac{5}{2}}} + \frac{1}{2u^{\frac{3}{2}}} + \frac{b^2}{u^{\frac{1}{2}}} \right) e^{-a^2/4u - b^2 u} \, du = -e^{b^2 t} \left[\frac{e^{-a^2/4u - b^2 u}}{u^{\frac{1}{2}}} \right]_0^t$$

$$= -\frac{e^{-a^2/4t}}{t^{\frac{1}{2}}}$$

Consequently, eliminating $-a^2/4u^{\frac{3}{2}}$, we have

$$b\sqrt{\pi} \mathscr{L}^{-1} \left\{ \frac{e^{-a\sqrt{s}}}{s + b\sqrt{s}} \right\} = e^{b^2 t} \int_0^t \left(\frac{ab}{2u^{\frac{3}{2}}} - \frac{b^2}{u^{\frac{1}{2}}} \right) e^{-a^2/4u - b^2 u} \, du$$

Now substitute $w = \frac{1}{2} a u^{-\frac{1}{2}} + b u^{\frac{1}{2}}$ so that

$$\frac{a^2}{4u} + b^2 u = w^2 - ab, \qquad dw = \left(\frac{b}{2u^{\frac{1}{2}}} - \frac{a}{4u^{\frac{3}{2}}} \right) du$$

Hence

$$\mathscr{L}^{-1} \left(\frac{e^{-a\sqrt{s}}}{s + b\sqrt{s}} \right) = \frac{2 e^{b^2 t + ab}}{\sqrt{\pi}} \int_\theta^\infty e^{-w^2} \, dw \qquad \text{where } \theta = b\sqrt{t} + \tfrac{1}{2} a / \sqrt{t}$$

$$= e^{b^2 t + ab} \operatorname{erfc} \theta \qquad\qquad \square$$

EXERCISES

Use the inversion theorem to find the functions whose Laplace transforms are:

1. $a^3 s (s^2 - a^2)^{-3}$.

2. $[s(as + 1) \dots (as + n)]^{-1}$.

3. $s^{-\frac{1}{2}} e^{-a/s}$.

4. $\dfrac{\sinh x\sqrt{s}}{\sinh l\sqrt{s}}, \qquad x < l.$

Chapter 5

Boundary Value Problems

5.1 Fundamentals As an illustration of the technique consider the solution of the linear partial differential equation

$$\frac{\partial^2 U}{\partial x^2} + A(x)\frac{\partial^2 U}{\partial t^2} + B(x)\frac{\partial U}{\partial t} + C(x)U = G(x,t), \qquad t \geqslant 0 \qquad (i)$$

where $U = U(x,t)$, x being a position coordinate and t the time. At time $t = 0$ we are given the following *initial conditions*:

$$U(x,0) = U_0(x) \qquad \text{for all } x \qquad (ii)$$

$$\partial U(x,0)/\partial t = U_1(x) \qquad \text{for all } x \qquad (iii)$$

where $U_0(x)$ and $U_1(x)$ are known functions of x which determine the initial position and initial rate of change of position of the given system. In addition to these initial conditions we are given a *boundary condition* which states that

$$E(x)U + F(x)\frac{\partial U}{\partial x} = H(x,t) \quad \text{at } x = x_0 \text{ for all } t \qquad (iv)$$

where E, F and H are known functions, and finally the condition that the solution for U is finite at infinity. To solve these equations, we define a Laplace transform with respect to the t-variable by $\int_0^\infty e^{-st}U(x,t)\,dt = u(x,s)$ assuming it exists. Again

$$\int_0^\infty e^{-st}\frac{\partial^2 U}{\partial x^2}dt = \frac{\partial^2}{\partial x^2}\int_0^\infty e^{-st}U\,dt = \frac{\partial^2 u}{\partial x^2}$$

and

$$\int_0^\infty e^{-st}G(x,t)\,dt = g(x,s)$$

Consequently equation (i) transformed in the usual way becomes

$$\frac{\partial^2 u}{\partial x^2} + A(x)(s^2 u - sU_0 - U_1) + B(x)(su - U_0) + C(x)u = g(x,s)$$

which is of the form

$$\frac{\partial^2 u}{\partial x^2} + P(x,s)u = Q(x,s) \qquad (v)$$

Since the boundary condition holds for all t we transform this also, so that at $x = x_0$

76

$$E(x)u + F(x)\frac{\partial u}{\partial x} = \int_0^\infty e^{-st}H(x,t)\,dt = h(x,s) \qquad \text{(vi)}$$

since $\qquad \displaystyle\int_0^\infty e^{-st}F(x)\frac{\partial U}{\partial x}\,dt = F(x)\frac{\partial}{\partial u}\int_0^\infty e^{-st}U\,dt = F(x)\frac{\partial u}{\partial x}$

Equation (v) is now solved as an *ordinary differential equation* with x as the independent variable, the solution yielding two arbitrary functions of s instead of the usual constants. These two functions are evaluated using (vi) with the condition of finiteness or its equivalent. Finally, when $u = u(x,s)$ is known its inverse, the required solution $U = U(x,t)$ is determined using the inversion theorem or otherwise. It should be verified that the solution obtained *does* indeed satisfy all the conditions of the given problem.

Problem 5.1   Solve the wave equation $c^2 \partial^2 U/\partial x^2 = \partial^2 U/\partial t^2$, $x > 0$, $t > 0$, subject to the boundary conditions $U(x,0) = \partial U(x,0)/\partial t = 0$ $x > 0$; $\partial U(0,t)/\partial x = F(t)$, $t > 0$.

Solution. In the notation of the previous section, taking the t-Laplace transform of the given equation and using the initial conditions at $t - 0$, $\partial^2 u/\partial x^2 = (s^2/c^2)u$ of which the solution is

$$u = A(s)e^{-sx/c} + B(s)e^{sx/c}$$

where A and B are arbitrary functions of integration. If the solution $U(x,t)$ remains finite as $x = \infty$ we must have $B(s) \equiv 0$ in order that $u \to 0$ when $x \to \infty$; this is the condition of finiteness referred to in section 5.1. We find A from the Laplace transform of the boundary condition at $x = 0$, i.e.

$$\int_0^\infty e^{-st}\frac{\partial U}{\partial x}\,dt = \frac{\partial}{\partial x}\int_0^\infty e^{-st}U\,dt = \frac{\partial u}{\partial x} = \int_0^\infty e^{-st}F(t)\,dt = f(s), \text{ say}$$

Using the solution for u with $B = 0$, $\partial u/\partial x = -(s/c)A(s)e^{-sx/c}$. Hence at $x = 0$ we have $f(s) = -(s/c)A(s)$ or $A(s) = -(c/s)f(s)$, so that the Laplace transform of the solution is

$$u = -\frac{c}{s}f(s)e^{-sx/c}$$

The inversion is found by using Rules 4 and 11. In fact, writing $-f(s)/s = g(s)$, and appealing to Rule 4,

$$U(x,t) = \mathscr{L}^{-1}\{g(s)e^{-sx/c}\} = G(t-x/c)H(t-x/c)$$

where

$$G(t) = \mathscr{L}^{-1}\{g(s)\} = \mathscr{L}^{-1}\{-cf(s)/s\} = -c\int_0^t F(v)\,dv$$

77

by Rule 11. Thus the solution is

$$U(x,t) = \begin{cases} G(t-x/c) & \text{for } t > x/c \\ 0 & \text{for } t < x/c \end{cases}$$

where

$$G(t) = -c \int_0^t F(v) \, dv. \qquad \square$$

It is simple to verify that all the conditions of the problem are satisfied by this solution.

5.2 Conduction of Heat in One Dimension   Let $U(x,t)$ denote the temperature at time t in a solid in which
   (i) heat flow takes place by conduction in one dimension only, parallel to Ox,
   (ii) there is no gain or loss of heat at any point P of the solid other than by conduction.
If K is the thermal conductivity, assumed constant, the rate of flow of heat per unit area across the plane $x = $ constant is given by $-K\partial U/\partial x$. The differential equation satisfied by $U = U(x,t)$ at every point P within the body is

$$\frac{\partial U}{\partial t} = k\frac{\partial^2 U}{\partial x^2}$$

where $k = K/c\rho$, c being the specific heat, and ρ the body density.
   To solve a particular problem we need to prescribe an initial condition such as at $t = 0$, $U(x,0) = F(x)$ (a given function), together with end conditions at $x = 0$ and $x = l$, say. These latter may be one of the following:
   (i) a given end temperature, or
   (ii) a given heat flux, or
   (iii) radiation into a medium of fixed temperature θ_0.
This last condition is expressed via Newton's law of cooling by

$$-K\frac{\partial U}{\partial x} = H(U-\theta_0)$$

where H is Newton's constant, i.e.
   $\partial U/\partial x + h(U-\theta_0) = 0, h = H/K > 0$ at $x = 0$ or l for all t

Problem 5.2   A semi-infinite solid filling $x \geqslant 0$ is initially at constant temperature U_0. Find the temperature distribution for $t > 0$, $x > 0$ when:

(i) the end $x = 0$ is kept at a temperature $F(t)$, $t > 0$, and consider the special case in which $U_0 = 0$ and $F(t) = Q(4\pi kt)^{-\frac{1}{2}}$

(ii) at the end $x = 0$ radiation takes place into the region $x < 0$ at temperature θ_0.

Solution. (i) We solve $\partial U/\partial t = k \partial^2 U/\partial x^2$ subject to the conditions $U(x, 0) = U_0$, $x > 0$; $U(0, t) = F(t)$, $t > 0$; $U(x, t)$ finite $x > 0$, $t > 0$.

Taking the t-Laplace transform of the differential equation, we have, with u denoting $\mathscr{L}\{U\}$,

$$su - U_0 = k \frac{\partial^2 u}{\partial x^2}$$

of which the solution is

$$u = s^{-1}U_0 + Ae^{-x\sqrt{(s/k)}} + Be^{x\sqrt{(s/k)}}$$

where $A = A(s)$, $B = B(s)$. Since $U(x, t) < \infty$ for all $x > 0$, $B \equiv 0$, i.e.

$$u = s^{-1}U_0 + Ae^{-x\sqrt{(s/k)}} \tag{1}$$

The condition $U(0, t) = F(t)$ implies $u(0, s) = \mathscr{L}\{F(t)\} = f(s)$, so that putting $x = 0$ in (1), $f(s) = s^{-1}U_0 + A$ which determines A. Thus,

$$u = s^{-1}U_0 + [f(s) - s^{-1}U_0]e^{-x\sqrt{(s/k)}} \tag{2}$$

The inverses of the components of the latter are

$$\mathscr{L}^{-1}\{s^{-1}U_0\} = U_0 \qquad \mathscr{L}^{-1}\{s^{-1}U_0 e^{-x\sqrt{(s/k)}}\} = U_0 \operatorname{erfc}\left(\frac{x}{\sqrt{(4kt)}}\right)$$

using Problem 4.4 or table, and since
$\mathscr{L}^{-1}\{e^{-x\sqrt{(s/k)}}\} = xe^{-x^2/4kt}/\sqrt{(4\pi kt^3)}$, by the convolution transform

$$\mathscr{L}^{-1}\{f(s)e^{-x\sqrt{(s/k)}}\} = \int_0^t \frac{xe^{-x^2/4ku}}{\sqrt{(4\pi ku^3)}}F(t-u)\,du$$

Using $\operatorname{erf} w = 1 - \operatorname{erfc} w$,

$$U(x, t) = U_0 \operatorname{erf}\left(\frac{x}{\sqrt{(4kt)}}\right) + \frac{2}{\sqrt{\pi}}\int_{x/\sqrt{(4kt)}}^{\infty} e^{-v^2}F\left(t - \frac{x^2}{4kv^2}\right)dv, \quad v^2 = x^2/4ku$$

which is solution for the temperature in case (i). In the special case $U_0 = 0$, $F(t) = Q(4\pi kt)^{-\frac{1}{2}}$, it is best to refer back to equation (2). Since

$$f(s) = \mathscr{L}\left\{\frac{Q}{\sqrt{(4\pi kt)}}\right\} = Q/\sqrt{(4ks)}$$

we have $u = Qe^{-x\sqrt{(s/k)}}/\sqrt{(4ks)}$. Using Problem 4.4,

$$U(x, t) = Qe^{-x^2/4kt}/\sqrt{(4\pi kt)}.$$

79

This represents one-dimensional *point* heat-source at $x = 0$ of strength Q. It satisfies the heat equation and $\int_{-\infty}^{\infty} U(x, t)\, dx = Q$ for all fixed $t > 0$.

(ii) In this case at $x = 0$ we have the condition $\partial U/\partial x + hU = h\theta_0$ which transforms to $\partial u/\partial x + hu = (h/s)\theta_0$. We use this to determine A in (1), for at $x = 0$,

$$\frac{\partial u}{\partial x} + hu = -A\sqrt{\left(\frac{s}{k}\right)} + h\left(\frac{U_0}{s} + A\right) = \frac{h\theta_0}{s}$$

Solving for A yields

$$u = \frac{U_0}{s} + \frac{h(\theta_0 - U_0)}{s(h - \sqrt{(s/k)})} e^{-x\sqrt{(s/k)}}$$

Since $b/(s(b + \sqrt{s})) = 1/s - 1/(b\sqrt{s} + s)$, using the results of Problem 4.4 with $a = x/\sqrt{k}$, $b = -h\sqrt{k}$ the inversion is

$$U(x,t) = U_0 + (\theta_0 - U_0)\left(\operatorname{erfc}\frac{x}{\sqrt{(4kt)}} - e^{-hx + h^2 kt}\operatorname{erfc}\theta\right)$$

where $\theta = (x - 2hkt)/\sqrt{(4kt)}$ $\qquad\qquad\qquad\qquad\qquad\qquad$ □

5.3 Longitudinal Vibrations of a Uniform Bar

We assume that the bar lies along the x-axis at any time t of its motion. If $U = U(x, t)$ denotes the displacement in the positive x-direction at any point x of the bar and $N = N(x, t)$ is the stress ρ the material density, F the body force per unit mass and E the Young's modulus, then from mechanics $N = E\, \partial U/\partial x$ and the differential equation satisfied by U is

$$\frac{\partial^2 U}{\partial x^2} - \frac{1}{c^2}\frac{\partial^2 U}{\partial t^2} = -\frac{F}{c^2} \qquad \text{where } c^2 = \frac{E}{\rho}.$$

Problem 5.3 A bar of length a hangs vertically under gravity with its uppermost point fixed at $x = 0$. At time $t = 0$ it is released from rest with the bar unstrained. Find for $t > 0$ (a) the general displacement $U(x, t)$, (b) the free end displacement, (c) the stress at the fixed end.

Solution. (a) Here the body force per unit mass is equal to g, the acceleration due to gravity, so that the equation for $U(x, t)$ is

$$\frac{\partial^2 U}{\partial x^2} - \frac{1}{c^2}\frac{\partial^2 U}{\partial t^2} = -\frac{g}{c^2} \qquad 0 < x < a, t > 0 \qquad\qquad\text{(i)}$$

Initially, there is no displacement or velocity, and therefore

$$U = 0 \quad \text{and} \quad \frac{\partial U}{\partial t} = 0 \qquad \text{for } t = 0, \qquad 0 < x < a \qquad\text{(ii)}$$

For all $t > 0$ there is no displacement at $x = 0$, i.e.

$$U = 0 \qquad \text{for } x = 0, t > 0 \tag{iii}$$

Also the end $x = a$ is permanently stress-free, i.e.

$$\frac{\partial U}{\partial x} = 0 \qquad \text{for } x = a, t > 0 \tag{iv}$$

Defining, $u = u(x, s) = \int_0^\infty e^{-st} U(x, t) \, dt$ and taking the transform of equation (i), we have

$$\frac{\partial^2 u}{\partial x^2} - \frac{1}{c^2} \left[s^2 u - sU(x, 0) - \frac{\partial U}{\partial t}(x, 0) \right] = -\frac{g}{c^2 s}$$

which by (ii) becomes

$$\frac{\partial^2 u}{\partial x^2} - \frac{s^2 u}{c^2} = -\frac{g}{c^2 s}$$

i.e.

$$u = g s^{-3} + A \cosh \frac{sx}{c} + B \sinh \frac{sx}{c} \tag{v}$$

where $A = A(s)$, $B = B(s)$ are determined by the transforms of (iii) and (iv), i.e. $u = 0$ when $x = 0$, $\partial u / \partial x = 0$ when $x = a$. Therefore $A = -gs^{-3}$, and $A \sinh(sa/c) + B \cosh(sa/c) = 0$.

Hence

$$u = \frac{g}{s^3} - \frac{g}{s^3} \frac{\cosh s(a-x)/c}{\cosh sa/c} \tag{vi}$$

The inverse of the first term is $\frac{1}{2} g t^2$. We need to use the inversion theorem to invert the second term. Consider

$$\int_{\sigma - i\infty}^{\sigma + i\infty} e^{st} \frac{\cosh s(a-x)/c}{\cosh sa/c} \frac{ds}{s^3}$$

Using the contour in Fig 4.1, there is a triple pole at $s = 0$ with residue

$$\lim_{s \to 0} \frac{1}{2!} \frac{d^2}{ds^2} \left[(s-0)^3 e^{st} \frac{\cosh s(a-x)/c}{s^3 \cosh sa/c} \right]$$

$$= \lim_{s \to 0} \frac{1}{2} \frac{d^2}{ds^2} \left[e^{st} \left(\cosh \frac{sx}{c} - \sinh \frac{sx}{c} \tanh \frac{sa}{c} \right) \right]$$

$$\lim_{s \to 0} \frac{1}{2} \frac{d^2}{ds^2} \left[e^{st} \left(1 + \frac{s^2 x^2}{2c^2} - \frac{s^2 xa}{c^2} O(s^3) \right) \right].$$

Using Liebnitz theorem this becomes,

81

$$\lim_{s \to 0} \tfrac{1}{2} t^2 e^{st} \left[1 + \tfrac{1}{2} x(x - 2a) \frac{s^2}{c^2} \right] + \lim_{s \to 0} t e^{st} x(x - 2a) \frac{s}{c^2} + \lim_{s \to 0} \tfrac{1}{2} e^{st} \frac{x}{c^2} (x - 2a)$$

$$= \tfrac{1}{2} t^2 + \frac{x(x - 2a)}{2c^2}$$

The remaining singularities are the zeros of $\cosh sa/c$ which give rise to simple poles at $s = \pm(2n + 1)\pi ci/2a$, $n = 0, 1, \ldots$. The residue at $s = is_n$ where $s_n = (2n + 1)\pi c/2a$ is

$$R_n = \lim_{s \to is_n} \left\{ (s - is_n) e^{st} \frac{\cosh s(a - x)/c}{s^3 \cosh sa/c} \right\}$$

Putting $s = i(s_n + \delta)$ and letting $\delta \to 0$, we have

$$\cosh \frac{i(a - x)(s_n + \delta)}{c} = \cos \frac{(a - x)(s_n + \delta)}{c} = \cos\left((2n + 1)(a - x) \frac{\pi}{2a} \right) + O(\delta)$$

$$\cosh \frac{ia(s_n + \delta)}{c} = \cos\left((2n + 1)\frac{\pi}{2} + \frac{a\delta}{c} \right) = (-1)^{n+1} \sin \frac{a\delta}{c}$$

$$= (-1)^{n+1} \frac{a\delta}{c} + O(\delta^2)$$

$$s - is_n = i\delta, \quad s^3 = -i(2n + 1)^3 \frac{c^3 \pi^3}{8a^3} + O(\delta), \quad e^{st} = e^{(2n+1)i\pi ct/2a} + O(\delta)$$

Hence substituting and letting $\delta \to 0$ we find

$$R_n = \frac{(-1)^n 8a^2}{(2n + 1)^3 \pi^3 c^2} \cos\left[(2n + 1)(a - x) \frac{\pi}{2a} \right] e^{(2n+1)i\pi ct/2a}$$

The residue at $s = -is_n$ is $\bar{R}_n$. Hence, the final expression for the inversion of (vi) is

$$U(x, t) = x(2a - x) \frac{g}{2c^2}$$
$$- \frac{16a^2 g}{\pi^3 c^2} \sum_{n=0}^{\infty} \frac{(-1)^n}{(2n + 1)^3} \cos(2n + 1)(a - x) \frac{\pi}{2a} \cos(2n + 1) \frac{\pi ct}{2a}$$

To find the displacement of the free end at $x = a$ we can either use this expression or put $x = a$ in (vi) and then invert the transform after expansion as follows. At $x = a$,

$$u(a, s) = \frac{g}{s^3} \left(1 - \frac{1}{\cosh sa/c} \right) = \frac{g}{s^3} \left(1 - \frac{2e^{-sa/c}}{1 + e^{-2sa/c}} \right)$$

$$= \frac{g}{s^3} (1 - 2e^{-sa/c} + 2e^{-3sa/c} - 2e^{-5sa/c} + \ldots)$$

Inverting by Rule 4,

82

$$U(a,t) = \tfrac{1}{2}gt^2 - g\left(t - \frac{a}{c}\right)^2 H\left(t - \frac{a}{c}\right) + g\left(t - \frac{3a}{c}\right)^2 H\left(t - \frac{3a}{c}\right)$$
$$- g\left(t - \frac{5a}{c}\right)^2 H\left(t - \frac{5a}{c}\right) + \ldots$$

Consequently,

$$U(a,t) = \tfrac{1}{2}gt^2 \qquad 0 < t < \frac{a}{c}$$

$$= \tfrac{1}{2}gt^2 - g\left(t - \frac{a}{c}\right)^2 \qquad \frac{a}{c} < t < \frac{3a}{c}$$

$$= \tfrac{1}{2}gt^2 - g\left(t - \frac{a}{c}\right)^2 + g\left(t - \frac{3a}{c}\right)^2 \qquad \frac{3a}{c} < t < \frac{5a}{c}$$

etc.

The physical interpretation of the structure of this solution is that the displacement propagates as an outgoing wave travelling with speed c, is reflected at the end $x = a$ after time a/c, and subsequently suffers infinitely many further reflections.

The stress $N = E\,\partial U/\partial x$ can be determined either by (a) or, writing

$$n = \mathscr{L}\{N\} = \int_0^\infty e^{-st} E\left(\frac{\partial U}{x}\right) dt = E\frac{\partial u}{\partial x}$$

we can use equation (vi) again, giving

$$n(o,s) = \frac{Eg}{cs^2}\frac{\sinh sa/c}{\cosh sa/c} = \frac{Eg}{cs^2}\left(\frac{1-e^{-\lambda}}{1+e^{-\lambda}}\right), \qquad \lambda = 2sa/c$$

$$= \frac{Eg}{cs^2}(1 - 2e^{-\lambda} + 2e^{-2\lambda} - 2e^{-3\lambda} + \ldots)$$

which by Rule 4 has the inverse

$$N(0,t) = \frac{Eg}{c}\left[t - 2\left(t - \frac{2a}{c}\right)H\left(t - \frac{2a}{c}\right) + 2\left(t - \frac{4a}{c}\right)H\left(t - \frac{4a}{c}\right) - \ldots\right]$$

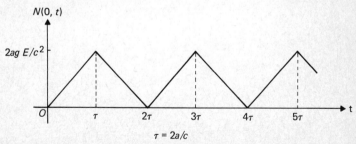

Fig. 5.1

83

Therefore, this stress at the fixed end $x = 0$ has triangular wave form illustrated in Fig. 5.1 with $N(0, t)$ reaching its maximum value $2agE/c^2$ when $t = (2n+1)2a/c$, $n = 0, 1, 2, \ldots$. $\qquad\qquad\square$

EXERCISES

1. Find the solution $U = U(x, t)$ of

$$\frac{\partial U}{\partial t} + \frac{\partial U}{\partial x} + U = xt, \qquad x > 0, t > 0$$

where $U(x, 0) = 0$, $t > 0$; $U(0, t) = 0$, $x > 0$.

2. Solve $\partial U/\partial t = k \, \partial^2 U/\partial x^2$, $x > 0$, $t > 0$, where $U(0, t) = F(t)$, $t > 0$; $U(x, 0) = 0$, $x > 0$.

3. A uniform horizontal bar of length a is at rest and unstrained when at $t = 0$ the end $x = 0$ is given a forced oscillation $p \sin qt$. Show that the motion of the end $x = a$ is given by

$$0 \qquad\qquad 0 < ct < a$$
$$2p \sin q(t - a/c) \qquad a < ct < 3a$$
$$2p[\sin q(t - a/c) - \sin q(t - 3a/c)] \qquad 3a < ct < 5a$$

4. Given that the displacement $U = U(x, t)$ of a taut vibrating string satisfies the equation

$$\frac{\partial^2 U}{\partial t^2} = c^2 \frac{\partial^2 U}{\partial x^2} \qquad 0 < x < l, t > 0$$

and $U(0, t) = 0$, $U(l, t) = 0$, $U(x, 0) = ax(l - x)$, $\partial U(x, 0)/\partial t = 0$, show that

$$U(x, t) = \frac{8l^2 a}{\pi^3} \sum_{n=1}^{\infty} \frac{1}{(2n-1)^3} \sin(2n-1)\frac{\pi x}{l} \cos(2n-1)\frac{\pi ct}{l}$$

Rule No.	Rule	Page

In particular, $\mathscr{L}\{(a-t)^n F(t)\} = e^{-as}\mathscr{D}^n(e^{as}f(s))$ 14

$\mathscr{L}\{t^n F(t)\} = (-\mathscr{D})^n f(s),$

$\mathscr{L}^{-1}\{\mathscr{D}^n f(s)\} = (-t)^n F(t)$ 37

6 $\mathscr{L}\{F(t)/(t+a)\} = e^{sa}\displaystyle\int_s^\infty e^{-xa}f(x)\,dx,\ a > 0$ 15

$\mathscr{L}^{-1}\left\{\displaystyle\int_s^\infty e^{-(x-s)a}f(x)\,dx\right\} = F(t)/(t+a)$

The corresponding results hold when $a = 0$ provided $\displaystyle\lim_{t\to 0+} F(t)/t$ exists.

7   If $F(t)$ is continuous for all $t > 0$, $F(t) = \mathrm{O}(e^{\sigma t})$ as $t \to \infty$,   17
$F'(t) \in$ class $\mathscr{A}$

$$\mathscr{L}\{F'(t)\} = s f(s) - F(0+)$$

or if $F(t)$ is continuous for all $t \geqslant 0$
$$\mathscr{L}\{F'(t)\} = s f(s) - F(0)$$

8   If $F^{(m)}(t)$ is continuous for all $t > 0$ and of exponential order   17
for $m = 0, 1, \ldots, n-1$ and $F^{(n)}(t) \in$ class $\mathscr{A}$,

$$\mathscr{L}\{F^{(n)}(t)\} = s^n f(s) - \sum_{m=0}^{n-1} s^{n-m-1} F^{(m)}(0+)$$

or if each $F^{(m)}(t)$ is continuous for all $t \geqslant 0$,

$$\mathscr{L}\{F^{(n)}(t)\} = s^n f(s) - \sum_{m=0}^{n-1} s^{n-m-1} F^{(m)}(0)$$

9   *First final s-limit rule*: $\displaystyle\lim_{s\to\infty} f(s) = 0$ when $F(t) \in$ class $\mathscr{A}$ 4

Second final s-limit rule: $\displaystyle\lim_{s\to\infty} s f(s) = F(0+)$ with the   17
conditions of Rule 7

10   *Zero s-limit rule*: under the conditions of Rule 7 with $\sigma = 0$ 18

$$\lim_{s\to 0+} s f(s) = \lim_{t\to\infty} F(t)$$

Rule No.	Rule	Page

11 $\quad \mathscr{L}\left\{e^{-at}\int_0^t e^{ax}F(x)\,dx\right\} = f(s)/(s+a)$ $\qquad\qquad$ 20

$\qquad \mathscr{L}^{-1}\left\{f(s)(s+a)^{-1}\right\} = e^{-at}\int_0^t e^{ax}F(x)\,dx$

$\qquad \mathscr{L}^{-1}\left\{f(s)(s+a)^{-n}\right\} = e^{-at}\int_0^t\int_0^t\cdots\int_0^t e^{at}F(t)\,dt^n$ $\qquad$ 38

$\qquad\qquad\qquad = e^{-at}\int_0^t e^{ax}F(x)(t-x)^{n-1}\,dx/(n-1)!$ $\quad$ 42

12 $\quad$ *Convolution transform:* Given $\mathscr{L}^{-1}\{f_1(s)\} = F_1(t)$, $\qquad$ 42
$\qquad \mathscr{L}^{-1}\{f_2(s)\} = F_2(t)$,

$\qquad\quad \mathscr{L}^{-1}\{f_1(s)f_2(s)\} = \int_0^t F_1(x)F_2(t-x)\,dx = F_1 * F_2$

$\qquad\qquad\qquad\qquad = \int_0^t F_2(x)F_1(t-x)\,dx = F_2 * F_1$

13 $\quad$ *Periodic function formula:* Given $F(t)$ is periodic with period τ $\quad$ 18
$\qquad$ and piecewise continuous in $0 < t < \tau$,

$\qquad \mathscr{L}\{F(t)\} = f_\tau(s)/(1-e^{-\tau s}),\, s > 0 \quad f_\tau(s) = \int_0^\tau e^{-st}F(t)\,dt$

14 $\quad$ *Heaviside formula:* Given polynomials $M(s)$, $N(s)$ of degree $\quad$ 44
$\qquad m$, n $(>m)$ respectively where $N(\alpha_k) = 0$ $k = 1,2,\ldots,n$,
$\qquad \alpha_k$ are all distinct and $M(\alpha_k) \neq 0$,

$\qquad\qquad \mathscr{L}^{-1}\{M(s)/N(s)\} = \sum_{k=1}^n e^{\alpha_k t}M(\alpha_k)/N'(\alpha_k)$

Table 2. List of Useful Laplace Transforms

$F(t)$	$f(s)$	Problem
$\cosh pt$	$\dfrac{s}{s^2 - p^2}$	1.1
$\sinh pt$	$\dfrac{p}{s^2 - p^2}$	1.1
$\cos qt$	$\dfrac{s}{s^2 + q^2}$	1.2
$\sin qt$	$\dfrac{q}{s^2 + q^2}$	1.2
$t \cos at$	$\dfrac{s^2 - a^2}{(s^2 + a^2)^2}$	1.17
$t \sin at$	$\dfrac{2as}{(s^2 + a^2)^2}$	1.17
$t^2 \cos at$	$\dfrac{2s(s^2 - 3a^2)}{(s^2 + a^2)^3}$	1.17
$t^2 \sin at$	$\dfrac{2a(3s^2 - a^2)}{(s^2 + a^2)^3}$	1.17
$\dfrac{\sin at}{t}$	$\tan^{-1} \dfrac{a}{s}$	1.18
$t^x, x > -1$	$\Gamma(x+1)s^{-x-1}$	—
$t^n, n \geqslant 0$	$n! s^{-n-1}$	1.4
$e^{at} t^n$	$n!(s-a)^{-n-1}$	1.12
$t^{-\frac{1}{2}}$	$\sqrt{\left(\dfrac{\pi}{s}\right)}$	1.5
$t^{n+\frac{1}{2}}, n \geqslant 0$	$\dfrac{(2n+1)(2n-1)\ldots 3.1}{(2s)^{n+1}} \sqrt{\left(\dfrac{\pi}{s}\right)}$	1.5
$H(t-a), a \geqslant 0$	$\dfrac{e^{-as}}{s}$	1.6
$\delta(t)$	1	1.7
$\sin at^{\frac{1}{2}}$	$a\left(\dfrac{\pi}{4s^3}\right)^{\frac{1}{2}} e^{-a^2/4s}$	1.25

$F(t)$	$f(s)$	Problem
$t^{-\frac{1}{2}}\cos at^{\frac{1}{2}}$	$\left(\dfrac{\pi}{s}\right)^{\frac{1}{2}}e^{-a^2/4s}$	1.9
$J_0(at)$	$\dfrac{1}{\sqrt{(s^2+a^2)}}$	1.10
$J_n(at)$	$\dfrac{(\sqrt{(s^2+a^2)}-s)^n}{a^n\sqrt{(s^2+a^2)}}$	1.20
$J_0(at^{\frac{1}{2}})$	$s^{-1}e^{-a^2/4s}$	1.26
$\ln t$	$\dfrac{\Gamma'(1)-\ln s}{s}$	1.27
$(\pi t)^{-\frac{1}{2}}e^{-a^2/4t}$	$s^{-\frac{1}{2}}e^{-a\sqrt{s}}$	4.4
$\operatorname{erf}t^{\frac{1}{2}}$	$\dfrac{1}{s\sqrt{(s+1)}}$	1.22
$\operatorname{erf}at$	$s^{-1}e^{s^2/4a^2}\operatorname{erfc}\left(\dfrac{s}{2a}\right)$	—
$e^{b^2t}\operatorname{erfc}(bt^{\frac{1}{2}}+\tfrac{1}{2}at^{-\frac{1}{2}})$	$\dfrac{e^{-ab-a\sqrt{s}}}{s+b\sqrt{s}}$	4.4
$t^m L_n^m(t) =$ $\dfrac{e^t}{n!}D^n(e^{-t}t^{n+m})$	$\dfrac{(n+m)!}{n!}\dfrac{(s-1)^n}{s^{n+m+1}}$	1.21

Answers to Exercises

Chapter 1

1. $\dfrac{6p^3}{(s^2-p^2)(s^2+9p^2)}$, $\dfrac{24p^4}{s(s^2+4p^2)(s^2+16p^2)}$, $\dfrac{s(s^2+7p^2)}{(s^2+p^2)(s^2+9p^2)}$.

   $\dfrac{s^4+16s^2p^2+24p^4}{s(s^2+4p^2)(s^2+16p^2)}$.

2. $3a^2/(s^3+a^3)$.

3. $\{s-\sqrt{(s^2-a^2)}\}^n/[a^n\sqrt{(s^2-a^2)}]$.

4. $\ln[(s^2+a^2)/(s^2+b^2)]$.

5. $e^{b(s-\sqrt{(s^2+a^2)})}/\sqrt{(s^2+a^2)}$, $(\tfrac{1}{2}a)^n s^{-n-1}e^{-a^2/4s}$

6. $[\Gamma'(n+1)-\Gamma(n+1)\ln s]s^{-n-1}$.

7. $s^{-\frac{1}{2}}e^{as}\operatorname{erfc}\sqrt{(as)}$.

8. $a\pi(1+e^{-as})/(a^2s^2+\pi^2)$.

Chapter 2

1. $t(2a-t)e^{-t/a}/(2a^4)$, $(2a^2-4at+t^2)e^{-t/a}/(2a^5)$.

2. $(1-e^{-t/a})^n/n!$

3. $(2\pi t^3)^{-\frac{1}{2}}\sin at$, $J_0(at)-atJ_1(at)$.

4. $\pi^{-\frac{1}{2}}\sinh\sqrt{(4t)}$.

5. $(\pi t)^{-\frac{1}{2}}\sinh\sqrt{(2at)}\sin\sqrt{(2at)}$, $(\pi t)^{-\frac{1}{2}}\cosh\sqrt{(2at)}\cos\sqrt{(2at)}$.

6. $e^{2t}(2\cos 3t+\tfrac{1}{3}\sin 3t)+e^t(\cos 2t+\tfrac{5}{2}\sin 2t)$.

7. $e^t(t+2)+e^{-2t}(\tfrac{1}{2}t^2-2t+3)$.

8. $\tfrac{1}{2}[1+(-\tfrac{1}{2})^n]$, $na<t<(n+1)a$.

Chapter 3

2. $\tfrac{1}{4}\int_0^t e^{-3(t-u)}\sin 4(t-u)F(u)\,du$, $e^{-3t}\cos 2t+e^{2t}\sin 4t$.

3. $J_1(t)/t$.

4. $X=e^{-t}+3e^t-\sin t+\tfrac{1}{2}t\cos t$, $Y=4e^t+(2-t)\cos t+(2+t)\sin t$.

5. $X=2e^{-t}-\cos t$, $Y=e^{-t}+\sin t$.

6. $a_n=(p^n-q^n)/\sqrt{5}$, $p=\tfrac{1}{2}(1+\sqrt{5})$, $q=\tfrac{1}{2}(1-\sqrt{5})$.

7. $X(t)=X(0)+(\sin p\pi/\pi)f(t)*t^{p-1}$.

8. $e^t/(1-e^{-a})$.

Chapter 4

1. $\frac{1}{8}t(at\cosh at - \sinh at)$.

2. $(1 - e^{-t/a})^n/n!$

3. $(\pi t)^{-\frac{1}{2}}\cos 2\sqrt{(at)}$

4. $\dfrac{2\pi}{l^2}\displaystyle\sum_{n=1}^{\infty}(-1)^{n-1}n\sin\dfrac{n\pi x}{l}e^{-n^2\pi^2 t/l^2}$

Chapter 5

1. $x(t - 1 + e^{-t}) - (t - 2 + 2e^{-t} + te^{-t}) + e^{-x}[t - x - 2 + 2e^{-t+x}$
   $+ (t - x)e^{-t+x}]H(t - x)$.

2. $\dfrac{x}{2\sqrt{(\pi k)}}\displaystyle\int_0^t \dfrac{e^{-x^2/4k(t-u)}}{(t-u)^{\frac{3}{2}}}F(u)\,du$.

Index